MW00559640

Aphrodisiacs
Aphrodite's Secrets
Sexuality, Sexual Dysfunction, and a History and A-Z of Aphrodisiacs

Linda Louisa Dell
BSc IIHHT MICHT FISCT MHFS

www.capallbann.co.uk

Aphrodisiacs
Aphrodite's Secrets
Sexuality, Sexual Dysfunction, and a History and A-Z of Aphrodisiacs

©Copyright Linda Louisa Dell

ISBN 186163 304 1
ISBN 13 9781861633040

Internal illustrations by J M Jomain
Cover design by HR Design
Photographs by Linda Louisa Dell

Published by:

Capall Bann Publishing
Auton Farm
Milverton
Somerset
TA4 1NE

Dedication

To lovers everywhere, be safe, be strong and be true to yourself.

According to Chinese history, Confucius (551-479 BCE) was a thinker, political figure and educator. He taught that in every relationship people have responsibilities and obligations to each other and that if these responsibilities are honoured then society will be just and harmonius.

Warning and Disclaimer

In this book I have tried to give some information relating to sexuality, sexual problems and sexual dysfunction that will help people that have suffered from sexual problems,

Making love can be a beautiful and natural experience, to be enjoyed and appreciated, sometimes though, problems arise that can spoil your enjoyment.

In this book I have listed many aphrodisiacs from the bizarre to the mundane some of which can help with sexual problems. I have to stress that much of the information given in the A-Z of aphrodisiacs is intended for curiosity only and that the effects of some herbs, plants and essential oils can be dangerous or vary from person to person and what is a safe dose for one can be very toxic for another. The author and publisher can take no responsibility for the mis-use of any of the preparations listed herein.

The information given is not intended to take the place of medical advice and attention.

I would recommend that you see your medical practitioner is you feel that you have any medical sexual problems. Do not be embarrassed to seek help, your doctor deals with similar problems every day and will not be shocked.

With the prevalence of AIDS and other sexually transmitted disease, if you do not practise safe sex you are risking your life and that of your partners.

I have attempted to include the Latin names for some plants in my A-Z of Aphrodisiacs, but I am not a botanist so I am sorry if my attempts are not accurate, may the purists among you please forgive any errors.

Contents Page

By the same author:

Can't Sleep, Won't Sleep
Dreamtime A History, Mythology, Physiology and Guide to the
  Interpretatiion of Dreams

Viagra Nasturale (natural Viagra) on sale on a market stall

Chapter 1

Low sex drive is very common and can affect up to one fifth of the population at any one time. In researching this book I was astonished at the enormous range of aphrodisiac substances, vitamins, minerals, herbs, essential oils and drugs that have, reputedly, a profound and beneficial effect on the libido. Jungians often use the name of the Greek god Eros to talk about the lover energy; they also use the Latin term *libido*. By this term they mean not just sexual appetite but a general appetite for life.

Sex Drive and Libido

Sex drive, or libido, is more often than not the strongest urge in humans after food and sleep. But all too often one partner ends up having a lower sex drive than another partner and the other can end up feeling frustrated, neglected or unloved.

Loss of sex drive is extremely common and is now the biggest single reason for consulting a sex therapist. A normal sex drive is needed as your sexual health and general well-being are very closely linked. Just as the healthier you are the more you are likely to want to have sex, increased sexual energy is also beneficial to the mind, body and the spirit.

The benefits of regular sex has been recommended throughout the ages, in ancient China, the flow of sexual energy round the body was believed to form the basis of physical, emotional and spiritual wellbeing and channelling sexual energy was considered the key to immortally. Herbal aphrodisiacs and erotic arts were therefore used not to increase simply pleasure in sex, but also as a means to advance general health and longevity.

The Greek physician, Galen, wrote in the 2nd century AD that sexual abstinence was the direct cause of hysteria, while in the 1940s psychoanalyst Wilhelm Reich advocated an orgasm a day for optimum health.

Many researchers have found numerous beneficial effects of indulging in regular sex, the 'little death' as the French call sexual climax, may help to postpone that eventual big death.

In men, hair growth seems to increase when sex is anticipated, probably as a result of increased testosterone activity. In both men and women levels of the hormone, oxytocin peaks during orgasm, having a tranquillising effect on both sexes helping to provide a good night's sleep, although the effect appears to be greater in men that in women.

Sex is good exercise; a vigorous lovemaking session can burn 500 kcals per hour and is a lot more fun than jogging. The sex drive or libido, is a powerful directing force that has a profound effect on human behaviour. The term libido was first used by the psychoanalyst, Sigmund Freud, to signify the instinctive psychosexual energy that is present in everyone from birth.

Men are said to reach their sexual peak in their teens, while their psychological sex drive peaks after the age of 50, when testosterone levels fall. Women are said to reach their physical sexual peak in their thirties or forties while their psychological sex drive reaches its maximum, in their 50s at the same time as that of males.

Losing Interest in Sex

Often even in a settled, loving, long term relationship the sensual thrills that accompanied the first flush of love will recede once the passionate honeymoon phase is over; love-making often becomes less exciting and even boring. Try to keep interest in sex alive by experimenting with different positions and techniques and varying the time and place of lovemaking so your love life does not become stale.

There can be many reasons for sex drive to fall or fail; these can include medical or life style situations such as;

• Familiarity or boredom
• Being unfit, overweight, having low self esteem.
• Stress and lack of sleep.
• Poor diet, excess alcohol, smoking and drugs.
• Pregnancy and breastfeeding.
• Anxiety and depression.
• Pain or illness.
• Menopause, period problems and hysterectomy.
• Impotence
• Male menopause, prostate problems and hypogonadism
• Previous sexual abuse and relationship problems
• Lack of sunshine SAD. (Seasonal Affective Disorder)
• Cultural influences and parents' attitude to sex.

Familiarity or Boredom

It may be that you are in a loving relationship, but things have got a bit predictable. If this is the case, try to bring some excitement back into your relationship, surprise your partner, try different positions, use sex aids, learn how to massage each other, take a romantic break together and if you have children get granny or someone to look after them at least once a week so you can just concentrate on each other and indulge yourselves without fear of interruptions.

Being Unfit, Overweight, and Having Low Self-esteem

General unfitness, lack of exercise, being over weight and not liking the way you look can certainly lower sex drive. The first thing to remember is that sex is an excellent exercise; you can lose between 200 and 500 calories in an average to spirited sex session.

In today's society, more people are becoming overweight which leads to sluggishness and low energy levels which leads to lack of self esteem and low sex drive. One of the most inhibiting factor when it comes to making love is lack of confidence in your body shape, women especially feel too fat, don't like their breasts or feel they have lost their shape, particularly after bearing children. It is important for you to love your body and love yourself and to always make your partner feel comfortable with his or her body image and sexuality. You do not have to be size ten to feel like a sexy woman, as most men will agree.

Stress and Lack of Sleep

Stress is one of the commonest causes of loss of libido along with overwork, tiredness and lack of sleep. Reducing stress levels will help to boost sex drive in both men and women. You should also aim to avoid coffee, strong tea and caffeinated drinks, cigarettes and alcohol when you are under stress as these only make matters worse. Lack of sleep can be caused by many things; working long hours, shift work, jet lag or even a new baby. (See my book, *Can't sleep, Won't Sleep*' for help with sleep problems.)

Poor Diet, Excess Alcohol, Smoking and Drugs

It is generally estimated that one in ten people do not get all the nutrients they need from their food alone, and need to take vitamin supplements to complement their diet. I would guess this figure could be even higher than that.

Alcohol in small quantities is an aphrodisiac, but only for women, alcohol makes men less discerning in their sexual partners and too much alcohol is definitely an anti-aphrodisiac and will encumber a male erection. Milk thistle can help to protect liver cells from the poisonous effect of alcohol and may help to boost testosterone levels that have been lowered by excess alcohol intake. Alcohol heightens our feelings, and lowers our inhibitions. Some people, men and women, become very aggressive under the influence of too much alcohol. Too much alcohol dampens the sexual urge and performance.

Many commonly prescribed drugs, and some illicit drugs, have a negative effect of sex drive. If you think your low sex drive is linked with a medication you are taking, consult your doctor, but do not stop taking your medication except under medical supervision.

Pregnancy and Breastfeeding

Sex drive can go up or go down or remain the same during pregnancy. Every woman and every pregnancy is difference. Psychological influences play a large part, as does increased blood flow to the genital area and increased lubrication in fact means that orgasm is usually easier to achieve and more intense.

If low sex drive occurs it is to do with levels of the libido neutralizing hormone prolactin. Some men find a pregnant woman sexually exciting, but many others are put off sex and often this is because of fear of harming the baby or changes in the female partner's pheromones.

After childbirth the female sex drive will normally return but sometimes when the women is breastfeeding high levels of the prolactin hormone will inhibit sexual feelings. This is a way of nature preventing the woman becoming pregnant again while her newborn is still very much dependent on her.

Other factors that may affect postnatal sex drive include being sore from stitches or being over stretched during childbirth, low self esteem, anxiety and body image. If low sex drive is linked with postnatal depression you must seek medical help from the doctor immediately.

Anxiety and Depression

Anxiety and depression can lead to physical tiredness, emotional exhaustion and loss of sex drive. Depression can be caused by many things, lifestyle changes, bereavement, illness and menopause. Always seek medical advice for depression and prolonged anxiety whatever the cause.

Pain or Illness

Physical discomfort when making love can lead to lack of interest or aversion to sex especially in females. Pain when making love may be superficial due to vaginal thrush, allergy, cystitis or vaginal dryness, or deep pain due to pelvic inflammatory disease. It can also come from pain in the hips, legs or back. In these cases care must be taken to find the correct positions that do not put stress on those limbs.

Many long term diseases such as those affecting the heart can lead to loss of sex drive, some sexual activity helps with a feel good factor even with long term illness, let your doctor be your guide here.

Menopause

Menopause is a natural time in a woman's life when her fertility draws to an end. It can affect women in two ways, relief and a new sexual freedom or remorse at the loss of a fertile body. The clitoris sometimes becomes less sensitive and this is probably the main cause of difficulty reaching orgasm after the menopause. Using a lubricant can help with a dry vagina which can be uncomfortable during intercourse.

Impotence

Impotence is the inability to perform sexually and the main feature is the failure to achieve an erection. There can be many causes for this either physical or emotional. The word impotence is derived from the Latin *impotentia* (lit: lack of power).

The first clinical definition appears in Copland's *Dictionary of Practical Medicine* in editions between 1833 and 1848. Later Strauss (1950) defines it as 'the inability to perform the sexual act'. Ernest Jonas (1918) declared it is "the complete or incomplete inability satisfactorily to carry out heterosexual coitus per vaginam. Satisfactory mean adequate erection, time and control of ejaculation."

Male Menopause, Prostate Problems and Hypogonadism

Male menopause is also a time when men experience a lowering of the libido due to the fall in testosterone levels in the body. Prostate problems can also be a factor. The tube through which urine flows from the bladder to the outside can be impeded and make an erection uncomfortable. Hypogonadism means underactive testicles. This is caused by underactivity and high prolactin levels. Male hypogonadism, results in low sex drive and fertility problems.

Previous Sexual Abuse and Relationship Problems

Low sex drive can result from relationship problems where one has simply fallen out of love with your partner and is no longer attracted to them. Unresolved anger, abuse and infidelity can also play important roles especially where the couple find it difficult to communicate. There may also be unresolved issues regarding sexual orientation, many wife abusers have homosexual tendencies that they have denied and then they take their frustration and aggression out on their partner.

Previous sexual abuse can carry over into a current relationship. Where this is a problem professional counselling may be needed.

SAD (Seasonal Affective Disorder)

Lack of sunshine, SAD, seems to have a dampening effect on the sex drive. Sunlight has an effect on the pineal gland in the brain and promotes desire and the readiness to mate. Many people find they feel sexier in hot sunny weather. Take a grapefruit supplement and in severe cases buy an ultra violet light box.

Cultural Influences and Parents' Attitude to Sex

Cultural attitudes to sex vary around the world and can have a profound effect on sex drive. In homes where sex is frowned on, parents are discreet about their sexual activity or never discuss sex, or where there is a non sexual, active single parent raising a child, low libido becomes the normal role model. This can have a subliminal effect on a child's own sexual attitudes in later life.

Negative social conditioning about sex inevitably creates fear, and this fear is passed from generation to generation by sometimes well-intentioned agents such as parents, teachers and religions. Fear also inhibits communication in sex, instead of being a deep communion between two people, love-making often becomes a tense encounter in which both partners are afraid to express their real needs.

The reduction of sex to a purely physical act also promotes an externalized idea of intercourse, in which lovemaking is perceived as a performance. "Did you come yet?" an anxious lover may ask.

We must release our inhibitions and allow ourselves to enjoy sex just for the sake of it, sex should be fun, self pleasure is not a sin, and our sexuality is a vital part of all our lives.

Masturbation

Religion, societies and some parents have specified that touching the sexual organs is taboo, let alone sexual pleasuring by masturbation. These parts of the body have been condemned and given coarse, ugly names; prick, bone, one-eyed trouser snake for the man, and slit, cunt, squeeze-box, and pussy for the female. Their dignity has been denied, their power diminished instead of celebrated. I want to make this very clear, there is nothing wrong with masturbation, it is healthy, and it is a good way to find out about your own body. And it can be included in your lovemaking with your partner or as a way of sexual release for those without a partner.

What is regular sex?

For some couples every night is normal, for others once a month is adequate. For most people once or twice a week is the norm. What is important is to find the right balance that satisfies both partners. If one partner is not as sexually active the less active partner should not object to the other partner masturbating. They can even lend a hand, so to speak. This could be something they can share and could bring them closer together.

Love, acceptance, support and understanding are what make a good and lasting relationship.

An African witchdoctor displaying aphrodisiac herbs

Chapter 2

An Introduction to Aphrodisiacs and Sexual Practices

Aphrodisiacs in History

Probably the first recorded reference to aphrodisiacs comes from undated Egyptian medical papyri believed to be from the Middle Kingdom, which flourished between 2200-1700 BCE. Aphrodisiacs are mentioned in the Bible and many of the world's sacred literature. Ancient narrative is filled with glowing accounts of aphrodisiac foods and potions. By the time of the golden age of Greece, their use was fairly commonplace. The Romans were also intimately familiar with the art of culinary seduction and the use of oils and perfumes. Aphrodisiac lore passed from the Roman to the early Christian era, through the Middle Ages and the Renaissance, and to modern times.

Pheromones

The word pheromone is derived from the Greek *pherin* (to bring or transfer to) and *hormone* (to excite.) The term accurately means to bring or give excitement and these chemicals appear to live up to their name. Pheromones are volatile substances that are produced by one individual to produce powerful sexual or behavioural responses in other members of the same species. They have a powerful and intense effect on the brain.

We all know that the most compelling sex organ in the human body is the brain. There are two types of sexual climax: ones in the body and ones in the brain.

It has been suspected for many years that pheromones play a role in human sexual behaviour, a woman's sensitivity to musk like odours is greatest around the time of ovulation. As a result, many expensive perfumes have, in the past, included secretions from the sexual glands of the musk deer and anal glands of the civet cat and ambergris from the intestine of the sperm whale.

Human pheromones are now known to be secreted in small amounts in skin oils around the nipples, under the armpits and in the genital area. They are related to DHEA and act at a primitive, subconscious level to attract the opposite sex. DHEA (Dehydroepiandrosterone) is a natural hormone synthesized by the adrenal glands from cholesterol. In medical terms, it is a 'precursor' of hormonal synthesis, like testosterone, estrogen and progesterone. Peak glandular extrusion is reached around age 21 and drops 90% by the age of 75.

Evolution designed us to secrete pheromones when we see someone we find attractive and when we get sexually aroused. Pheromones are therefore an important key to human sexual attraction and although they are mostly undetectable at a conscious level, have powerful effect on our mood.

Yin and Yang

Sexual union between man and woman was the basic concept behind Yin and Yang and to the ancient Chinese complemented the forces of life. The Chinese believed that sexual union has a cosmic influence on world events. According to R. H. Gulik, "Ancient China considered the clouds to be earth's ova, which are fertilized by the rain, heaven's sperm." Yin and Yang depended upon the harmony between a man and a woman, and as a woman is slower to be aroused and to reach orgasm than a man, it would be up to him to preserve the harmony and satisfy her needs by practising the 'Tao of Loving'. Man is fire, which quickly flares up and can easily be extinguished. Woman is water, which takes longer to heat up, but once hot cools down slowly. 'Fire is extinguished by water and water is heated by fire.'

Many Chinese herbs such as ginseng, are useful in strengthening sexual potency, aromatic spices and herbs were used regularly both to enhance sexual union and to promote harmony between the two partners.

Japan

Such was the Japanese understanding of the importance of sexual expression that the genitals were worshipped. Ancient fertility festivals frequently culminated in a sexual free-for-all.

Phallic worship is one of the oldest aspects of religion in Japan and even today a shrine exists in Kanamara with a giant wooden phallus on which grandmothers sit their small granddaughters in the hope that they will receive good luck for a fertile and happy marriage.

Japanese Pillow Books

Pillow books have been a traditional gift exchanged between lovers. They take their name from the lacquered wooden pillows of Japan in which these conveniently small works or erotic instruction and amusement were traditionally kept. The first pillow book to bear the evocative title was written by a Japanese noblewoman early in the 14th century, but erotic gift books have been enjoyed by lovers in China and India for many thousands of years.

Taoist Sex

Sex puts a sparkle in the eye,
a glow to the cheeks
and makes the world seem like a better place.

Mantak Chia, *Taoist Secrets of Love.*

Over two thousand years ago Taoist physicians studying sex concluded that sex is necessary to the physical, mental and spiritual well-being of men and women. Also a man whose lovemaking skills enable him to enjoy prolonged and frequent sexual functioning is more highly rated than a man who is merely young and handsome. According to Taoist belief, energy and impetus are the source of a fulfilling existence. In the universal picture humans are relatively small. In order to maintain a dynamic balance of health we must be in accord with the source that is the immeasurable power of nature.

Today we are taught to look outside ourselves for entertainment and constantly seek new stimulation to satisfy this need. Yet hidden within ourselves are unlimited electrifying ecstasies that we can never tire of. Young people today become easily bored and need to be constantly entertained. They have lost the ability to be themselves. They are constantly emulating others and are slaves to peer pressure or led like zombies by the media hype of the day.

Taoism is not a cult, a religion nor a path to salvation; the Tao is the boundless force of nature, the path of the heart or put simply 'the way'. The raw materials needed for the Tao can be found, within ourselves, at any given moment in our lives. The Taoists, being practical, proposed that we begin with the most accessible energy which is the feeling of sexual attraction and the need to procreate. Unlike Tantra, Taoism never took on secret rituals and invocation of religious deities. Sex was more openly used in China as a medicinal form of healing and natural way to spiritual balance. There are two main goals for which Tao technique of energy cultivation can be used:

• The first is to improve global happiness, to increase physical, emotional and mental satisfaction. For example, strengthening love partnerships, alleviating sexual frustration, impotency and premature ejaculation and relieving monotony with sex, increasing longevity and good health.

• The second is for someone on a spiritual pathway who desires to integrate sexual longing with his spiritual belief or meditative practice. The Tao is a sex-positive approach that helps to better integrate sexuality with spiritual growth.

The beginning stages of Taoism if you have a lover are:

1. A man learns to sustain erection for as long as desired and regulates his ejaculation.

2. Both partners re-direct sexual energy through the body into higher regions of the heart and brain.

3. The lovers exchange their super charged energy with each other.

If you do not have a partner you can follow what is called 'single cultivation'; this is where your sexual energy is channelled productively into your daily life and used to restore the mind, body and spirit and so enjoy life without sexual frustration.

Tantric Sex

"Tantra is a cult of ecstasy, a personal religion based on the mystical experience of joy rather than established dogma, sex is holy to a Tantric."

Kamala Devi. *The Eastern Way of Love.*

Tantra or Tantric sex is the Indian equivalent of Taoist sex. The major difference is that Tantra is seen to be a step on the road to spiritual enlightenment and mystical union, whereas practising Taoist sex does

Wall paintings in the Palace in Rajasthan

not require a religious belief system, simply the development of willpower. Tantra was born in India around 5000 BCE through the cult of the Hindu god Shiva and his consort, the goddess Shakri. Shiva was worshipped as the embodiment of pure consciousness in its most ecstatic state, and Shakti as the embodiment of pure energy. The Hindus believed that through uniting spiritually and sexually with Shiva, Shakti gave form to his spirit and created the universe. Tantra, therefore, view the creation of the word as an erotic act of love. The Hindu words for the genital organs are *lingam* for man and *yoni* for the woman, and these organs which to us are associated with sex, birth, and nature have in Indian culture a much more spiritual association. Just as in Christian theory the origin of the world is the Garden of Eden, Adam and Eve, so in India the god Shiva and his mighty lingam are believed to have brought the world to life. India's blatant enjoyment of sex has provided the world with the famous sex manual the *Kama Sutra* by the Indian nobleman and sage Mallanaga Vastsyayana. The *Kama Sutra* or *Kama Shastri* means 'Scripture of love.' as Kama is the Hindu word for love and is the equivalent of Eros or Cupid. The *Kama Sutra* has many references to herbs and aromatics as intrinsic parts of the sexual act.

In Tantric practice before sexual intercourse the woman is worshipped as the embodiment of the creative force Shakti. Her body parts are then anointed with different perfumes to honour her creative role and lift up her psyche so that she can manifest as a goddess. In the 'Rite of the Five essentials', so called because all five senses would be aroused, the finest oil of jasmin is applied to the hands, oil of patchouli to the neck and cheeks, essence of amber or hina musk to the breast, extract of spikenard to the hair, musk from the musk deer to the genitals, oil of sandalwood to the thighs, and essence of saffron to the feet. The men are also anointed over their body with sandalwood oil.

What is the Tantra a mystic cult, a magic ritual, a belief, a philosophy or a spiritual practice? It is difficult for many westerners to understand its meaning and its aims without giving in to the emotion to oversimplify and trivialize it. What is more the Tantra refers to the male and female sexual organs, as well as the sexual act itself, which is regarded as the symbol of sacred beliefs and divine bliss and its means of attaining the ultimate goal through orgasm.

Wall paintings in the Palace in Rajasthan

Centuries of religious and moral teachings, with their concepts of original sin and guilt, have clouded our minds so that it is difficult for us to accept that the sexual act can be a joy, a blessing and a means to attain ultimate inspiration by performing it in a very precise way, by following a set liturgy and saying the appropriate mantras or prayers. Tantra branched out and influenced not only the Hindu but also the Taoist and Buddhist traditions. Tantra influenced Western religious history through the ecstatic cult of the Greek god Dionysus around 2000 BCE. Tantra means 'weaving' in the sense of unifying, Tantra also means 'expansion'. We grow and expand into joy.

According to the Hindus, the Tantra is an essential part of Santana Dharma their original and eternal religion. Its basis rests on the what the Hindus still call Shakti, which is no other than the divine force the Divine Mother or the Mother Goddess the wife of Shiva, whose name can be translated literally as 'good' or 'kind'.

Shiva is the third god in the Trimurti of Hindu divinities comprising Brahma, Vishnu and Shiva. Shiva is seen as the incantation of the supreme Truth the transcendental absolute. Although Shakti the Divine Mother is seen as the wife of Shiva, Shiva nonetheless consorts with the female deities who represent the chakras. Each chakra correspond-ing to an appropriate Shakti which is its divine power. The seventh and last supreme chakra does not have is own Shakti since it is already one in itself.

The Yogi or ascetic, who devotes himself to one of the chakras, activates therefore the forces of the Shakti which are within him. As a result of the union which he kindles between Shiva and Shakti, the supreme Shakti, Kundalini Shakti, he can then achieve enlightenment.

Lakshmi is the goddess of happiness, whose name means 'good luck' and legend says that, like Aphrodite, she was born out the of the ocean's foam she is often represented as standing in the middle of a lotus flower.

Indian fertility Goddess

Smell

All of us have our own individual smell, which is as unique as our fingerprints. We can not always detect it ourselves because our noses become satiated with one smell after a very short period of time, just as when we apply perfume and cannot smell it after half an hour or so. Your individual aroma is effected by your lifestyle, what you eat and drink and if you smoke or bathe sufficiently or correctly. Desire, anger and fear can also alter your smell as your body releases adrenalin. Smell has very strong erotic connotations, and we can be attracted or repelled to another person by the way they smell. Part of loving or desiring someone is loving their smell. Some North African tribes give so much credence to personal aroma that the wife can be instantly divorced if she does not smell right.

Sexual excitement causes all sorts of exotic odours to emanate from the body, from the breath, the skin and in particular from the genitalia. In many successful relationships the partners are able to recognize each other's smells, as the body's natural perfume is indeed a potent method of nonverbal communication.

Sexual excitement causes the skin, breath, nipples and sexual organs to release exotic odours and these natural body perfumes can be enhanced by the subtle of essential oils. Courtesans of medieval Europe used to wear a little of their vaginal secretions as perfume, dabbing it behind their ears, necks and on their chests. They found it to be a strong sexual attractant.

Smell has been linked with the 'sixth sense', which is linked with our instinctive feelings about people. Homing in on these feelings can help us to read individuals better and this can be very useful within a sexual relationship. We can become more in-tuned with our partners moods and sexual needs. (Perfume your lips, mouth and genitals with rose water to smell and taste delightful.)

Pubic Hair

The ladies of the night of ancient Japan kept their pubic hair carefully plucked and clipped, and allegedly a knowledgeable man could allegedly "tell the degree of a woman's' sexual skill by a mere glance at how she pruned her shrubbery", (Geisha).

Shaving your pubic hair is a bold step to take, and it itches when growing back. But trimming your pubic hair into a tidy groomed shape is very easy and not at all uncomfortable, in fact it is very much more hygienic. A friend of mine, who does body waxing, is regularly asked to shape women's and men's pubes into hearts, especially around Valentines Day. And because hair retains fragrance, after a trim, lotion can be applied so that a gentle fragrance will emanate from your pubic hair. Floral waters (hydrosols) of rose, neroli or patchouli are popular and you can create your own signature scent.

"A woman is like a fruit which will only yield its fragrance when rubbed by the hands. Take for example, the basil; unless it is warmed by the fingers it emits no perfume. And do you not know that unless amber be warmed and manipulated it retains its aroma within? The same with woman; if you do not animate her with your frolics and kisses, with nibbling of her thighs and close embraces, you will not obtain what you desire."

Sheik Nefzawi *The Perfumed Garden*

It's all in the Mind

Sexual response begins in the mind; we have all heard or said 'I'm not in the mood'. In his *Taoist Secrets of Love*, Mantak Chia says, "Sex really begins well in advance of the act, as the energies you accumulate then will express themselves when you go deep into sex; try to calm down any feeling of agitation or anger, as this, more than anything else will block the flow of sexual energy ..."

Closing down the emotions to one's partner could easily have the effect of blocking the energy flow to outer parts of the body, for example to the hormone system. Temporary inability to achieve an erection can happen to any man at some time in his life. Causes can be physical exhaustions, ill health, the side effects of prescription drugs, or unspoken resentments towards his partner, blocking the flow of energy or chemical messages to the sex organs.

Zinc

Every time a man ejaculates he loses 2.5 mg of zinc, and although zinc is found in many natural foods, if a man is not eating a balanced diet then his zinc levels may become greatly depleted.

Next to impotence the problem men fear most is premature ejaculation. Tension can be a major cause of premature ejaculation, when there is a sudden build-up of energy in the penis; perhaps the man has not had sex for a period of time or he is tense, especially in the abdomen and buttocks. Baths with 10 drops of lavender oil can be very helpful for this problem.

Oral Sex

In India and China oral sex has always been considered a normal part of the art of loving and in an eastern book called *The Golden Lotus* we find a sweet poem about the playing of the flute.

> Not from bamboo or stone, not played on strings,
> This is the song of an instrument that lives...
> Who can say what the tune is, or the key

In India where the AIDS virus is now a grave situation, young people have been recommended to indulge in oral sex by preference as being the safer option.

Kissing

Kissing is an important facet of lovemaking for several different reasons and has been written about at length in the *Kama Sutra*. The lips and tongue echo the labia and the penis. According to the ancient

Chinese sex annual the *Art of Bedchamber*, a man is like fire and a woman like water. The fire easily flares up but the water take s a longer time to boil. Kissing is a necessary and very enjoyable part of foreplay. (See chapter 8)

Oldest Aphrodisiac

Several aphrodisiacs have been popular since the days of antiquity. The mandrake plant is mentioned in the Old Testament is still used today. Mandrake or (*mandragora, mandragora officinarum*) is part of the potato family with a large dark brown root and small red fruits. It contains the alkalis atropine and scopolamine. In mild doses these are soporific; in larger doses they can kill. In antiquity there were magical rules for harvesting the plant. Pliny noted that the plant roots were in the form of human genitals which explains the idea of sympathetic magic and the supposed aphrodisiac effect.

Cantharides is another ancient aphrodisiac that was first mentioned by Aristotle: its active principle cantharidine is extracted from the dried and powered bodies of the blister beetle, a brown or bluish creature found in Southern Europe.

Ginseng was another old aphrodisiac the 'mystic plant of the orient', made into tablet by modern sex aid retailers and also put into wine and teas. There is, in the Far East today ginseng wine that is termed kaoling and it is as strong as vodka. The roots of ginseng are soaked in the cask for at least three years. It is recommended to take a small glass of the wine before bed for its stimulatory effect. (See chapter 9)

The Most Bizarre Aphrodisiac

Some of the most bizarre concoctions have been devised with the aim of restoring failing sexual powers. They can be plants with a resemblance to the human genital organs, but the most bizarre types of aphrodisiac are those involving an element of cannibalism.

We know of the use of parts of non human animals to increase human potency; tiger penis and rhino horn, (a Chinese Emperor, for example, kept a herd of deer so he could drink their blood to increase his virile power). But often it was thought desirable also to consume parts of men and women for this purpose. Menstrual blood, placenta and genitals have all been devoured to increase sexual prowess; semen was also popular. The semen of virile young men should be mixed with the excrement of hawks or eagles and taken in pellet form. Chinese eunuchs, seeking regeneration of their lost sexual organs, would hopefully eat the warm brains of newly decapitated criminals.

The famed aphrodisiac power of rhino horns is a myth, and a man would have a better chance by strapping the horn on to himself. Thankfully these splendid creatures are now protected in the wild and poachers are heavily penalized.

Chaucer recommended garlic, onions leeks, mushrooms and frogs' bone as an aphrodisiac. Some ancient recipes or aphrodisiacs are very peculiar and include body hairs. One recipe from the Middle Ages requires 6 pubic hairs and 6 hairs from the left armpit. The hairs would then be burned on a hot shovel and powdered. The resulting fine particles are then inserted into a piece of bread and the bread dipped in soup and fed to a lover to rekindle his/her sexual interest.

Like body parts and certain foods, precious stones and pearls have been associated with the power to stimulate sexual desire, not only when presented as gifts, but also when consumed. Pulverized agate is supposedly especially effective. Cleopatra dissolved pearls in vinegar and honey, and then sipped this beverage. She had beautiful skin and hair that glowed with vitality and given that she managed to seduce both Julius Caesar and Marc Anthony as lovers, the potion must have been the reason for her success?

Precious gemstones have also been pulverized and used as makeup on the eyes and Ancient Persians used crushed peals and rubies, gold dust and ambergris to make pastilles that they ate as an aphrodisiac.

In South America some women have served coffee filtered through their well worn knickers to the objects of their desire. A common aphrodisiac in ancient Rome was to take a cow's vulva and clean it well, put it to marinate in white wine add chopped onion, celery, fennel, saffron, pepper corns, ginger and salt. Cook for several hours then roll it in flour and brown it; serve with lemon juice.

Most Complicated Frigidity Cure

For one of the most bizarre cures for frigidity, linked to magic, it was necessary to search out a particular species of red bat which was resting in pairs amid the red flowers of a banana tree. The bats were dried, ground into powder and honey and then spread on the woman's sexual organs to make her feel sexy.

The Perfumed Garden

Umar ibn Mahammed al-Nefzawi is the author of the *Perfumed Garden* he lived in Southern Tunisia. He produced his remarkable erotic manual and in the preface it says that the author was animated by the most praiseworthy intentions.

The introduction itself warns that the work is not to be considered as a lascivious, erotic or obscene text. The highly motivated Sheik begins; *Praise be given to god, who has placed man's greatest pleasure in the genitalia of women and has designed the genitals of man to afford the greatest enjoyment to women.*

The subjects of this manual range from sexual physiology to generation. One chapter is devoted to men who are held in contempt, another discusses women who deserve to be praised. The deceits and treacheries of women in erotic matters are exposed. Medicines, aphrodisiacs and sexual rites are discussed with great precision and lucidity.

Chapter 3

Sex Magic

Love and sex rituals are as old as time itself, love and desire focused through herbs, flowers, sunshine, moonlight and fertilizing rain. The Goddess Mother and the cosmos are asked to help in spell casting. Sex magic is very potent and should always be performed without malice. Any malevolence is returned to the practitioner threefold.

Sex magic can add passion to an existing relationship or boost fertility, by reconnecting with the ancient earth energies and festivals of the natural world that linked our ancestors' fertility with the land itself. The four elements are represented by flowers and herbs, crystals, such as salt, fires, represented by candles and incense, and flowing water in the natural magic practised by our ancestors to bring love and fertility into their lives.

There is a long history of spells that can make one more attractive to a partner, 'Glamours', and there are spells to incite lust in another. But I would advise great caution in casting spells to have your will forced on another; these types of spells often have a bite in the tail and do not always turn out to your advantage.

Sex magic began in the form of fertility rites for the survival of the races. But they have survived as evidence from early pre-literate societies shows; in ancient stone figurines that celebrated the sacred female, and animals on which tribes depended for food and clothing, by a process of sympathetic magic. In the early hunter-gather societies the Earth Mother was worshipped as the giver of all life and fertility and thus regarded as sacred. The Venus of Willendorf, the earliest fertility figurine, dates from around 24,000-22,000 BCE and is made of limestone. It has voluptuous breasts, buttocks, thighs, a swollen stomach and protruding genital area.

The horn and its obvious association with the phallus became a symbol of male potency and courage, but still recognised the sanctity of the woman as the giver of life. This is probably where the myth of rhino horn aphrodisiac came from. This male potency symbol has survived the passage of time in such festivals as the annual Abbots Bromley Horn dance in September and in ancient bull worship traditions.

As the sky gods gained supremacy over the Earth Mother, tall pillars, stones and towers as well as small phallic stones made of jade or precious metals were created as emblems of male sexual potency.

No sex magic was complete without summoning up Venus or Aphrodite as a classical goddess of love to aid the petitioner and many modern spell casters still follow the custom of invoking the ancient god forms. Few people now celebrate the old festivals of love and fertility except in a commercialised sense.

In earlier times, the fertility of the people and the fertility of the soil were inextricably linked. Couples made love in the woods or fields at times of sowing or harvest, re-enacting the Sacred Marriage between the Sky Father or Horned God and the Earth Mother, symbolically fertilising the crops as well as ensuring their own fecundity. The Sacred Marriage is one that permeates all cultures, representing the union of male and female and it is one of the early creation myths.

There is a lovely image of Nut, the Egyptian Sky Goddess, her body made completely of stars, covering the horizontal Geb or Seb the Earth god, who in Heliopolian creation myths created Osiris, Isis and the darker Egyptian deities Seth and Nephthys. Another pair comes from the Maori traditions; Rangi the Sky Father and Papa the Earth Mother, are locked in an eternal embrace as they created the world. As the sky gods gained supremacy, they married the Earth goddess and she became the patroness of women.

Times of Year for Sex Magic:

• Early spring, the Spring Equinox January 30th until around March 21st.

• Brigantia, Imbolc or Oimelc the Celtic festival of Ewe's Milk held from sunset on January 31st until sunset of February 2. The original Brighde or Brigid is celebrated at the festival, the maiden aspect of the Triple Goddess.

• Valentines Day 14th February, St Valentine according to legend was a young priest who defied an edict of the Emperor Claudius 11 that soldiers should not be allowed to marry. St Valentine conducted the wedding of a number of young soldiers and was executed on February 14th AD 269.

• Summer Solstice or Longest day this falls on 21st June. This period is good for sex magic and for open air ceremonies, woodland weddings, and fertility festivals.

• Late summer festivals of Lammas or Lughnassadh around June 21st until July 31st. Male and female energies are high and excellent for sex magic and sacred sexuality.

• The Autumn Equinox runs for the three days from sunset on 22 September. It is the celebration of the harvest and abundance.

• The 31st of October in the beginning of the Winter Solstice or Shortest day. An ideal day to reinforce a mature or established relationship.

• Midwinter Solstice or Christmas runs from the shortest day December 20th for three days.

The Cerne Abbas Giant

The Cerne Abbas Giant, located in Dorset in England, is a true fertility icon whose powers have been credited with many pregnancies. The giant may be more than two thousand years old, representing either the fertility God Hercules or a Celtic deity of fertility.

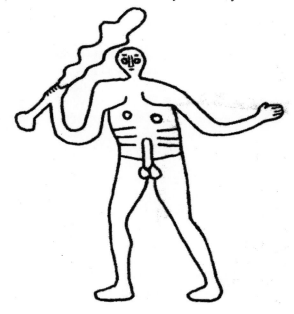

The Cerne Abbas Giant

There are countless sacred rocks or cave paintings, for example the aboriginal phallic creator Rainbow Snake, Jarapiri, at Jukulta Cave in the Tanamai Desert in Australia, and rock sculptures.

Alphaism

Alphaism, is the practice of magical chastity where the magician has no emotions or fantasies about sex between the occasions of sexual intercourse, is the first degree of sex magic. Physical chastity is prized; and more importantly, sexual interest and imagination are reserved for the time of actual sexual congress. Sex magic places the sex act upon a high, idealistic plane. It lifts sex play from the lowest plane of desire to the highest plane of self transformation.

Dianism

The second degree of sex magic is called Dianism, derived from the chaste goddess, Diana. Dianism is sexual congress without climax or orgasm. Participants should be tender and ardent, yet not allow themselves to reach orgasm. Practise in this art eventually produces a condition in which there is no sense of frustration even though orgasm is not reached. Rather than allowing themselves to be submersed in the full flow of pleasurable sensation the participants should allow the ecstasy to feed the fires of aspiration and inspiration. The aim of Dianism lies in continuing the union until such time as one goes into the 'borderland state,' an imaginative realm; this is similar to the yoga stage of Kundalini.

Kundalini

Kundalini is described as a primal psychic force or 'coiled sleeping serpent' that lies at the base of the spine. In kundalini yoga the goal is to awaken or arouse the kundalini, encouraging it to climb up through the body's power centres, 'chakras'. The aim is to achieve ultimate enlightenment by encouraging the energetic flow of kundalini to illuminate the brain. It is also use to promote sexual ecstasy and prolongs sexual activity.

A damiana liqueur at this point is perfect as a physic aphrodisiac, rekindling the flame to lengthen the borderland mood.

According to the author, folklorist and scholar of magic Zora Neale Hurston, "Magic is older than writing, so nobody knows how it started". Very true, but what we do know is that sex magic comes from all over the globe. There is not a people or culture on earth that did not at one time possess a magical tradition.

Chapter 4

Sexual Dysfunction

or the Freudian scientists at the beginning of the 20th century, sexuality was all in the head. Towards the end of the century, a molecular biologist attributed it to the defective male sexual organ. Psychopathy assumed that in almost all cases of sexual problems, particularly impotence, there were deeply repressed, unresolved and unconscious conflicts. Psycho-analysis was used as a tool to resolve such conflicts as it was believed that a uniform sexual response was the result of a uniform childhood experienced and parental taboos and attitudes. The Kinsey Report did not, however, subscribe to this view. This report was a pioneering document with a modern scientific approach to the study of sex.

In the sixties Mrs Virginia Johnson and Dr William Masters conducted laboratory research on human sexual response and human sexual inadequacy. They created special packages of sexual training programmes. Johnson and Masters integrated behavioural training and Psycho-education but their programmes were too extensive and required a longish period with intercourse and exercises. There were also other difficulties and these made the programmes inoperable.

Today there are three major approaches to sexual problems; the psychological, which aims at resolving psycho-sexual conflicts and marital relationships; the behavioural approach with focuses on pleasure giving techniques; and the physical therapies that use non-invasive vacuum devices, invasive and painful injection vasodilator drugs as well as surgery; vascular and implants.

Other medications are still on trial; the widely acclaimed marvel drug Viagra has also proved to be effective only in certain cases. It is contra-indicated in patients with heart ailments; more important it does not arouse sexual desire only bodily function.

There are also the aphrodisiacs such a cantharides made from dried beetles which are widely touted as effective but have been found to be particularly harmful. They are said to cause irritation in the urinary and the genital tract and can also cause infection, scarring and a burning sensation in the mouth and the throat. Thus we can see that modern medicine is still in an experimental stage when it comes to aphrodisiacs.

What Leads to Sexual Inadequacy

• Psychosomatic factors: Sexual desire can cease owing to bitter thoughts, anger and similar feelings. Nor getting the partners of ones choice or being forced to engage in sex against ones wishes and fighting against instinctive sexual desires, such as homosexuality, are some circumstances which can cause impotence. The mind plays a prominent a role in any kind of sexual activity. The centre in the brain with issues commands has to be activated. Yoga and other physical regimen can play a useful role in enhancing and regulating sexual activity.

• Dietetic factors: Excessive consumption of foods which by nature is acidic, salty, and pungent or heat producing, in the Ayurvedic sense of the term, can dry up the watering principle or the organism and cause impotence.

• Over-indulgence in sex: virile impotence can be caused by over-indulgence in sex or sexual addiction by those who are exhausted, aging or promiscuous and do not resort to the use of suitable aphrodisiacs.

• Celibacy: The practice and the constant suppression of the sexual urge by those who believe in austerity can result in permanent damage to the semen-producing organs of the male body.

• Sexually transmitted diseases: Diseases such as syphilis which affect the male generative organ and other injuries which destroy the spermatic cord thoroughly damage the ability for coition.

• Congenital defect: Impotence can be caused by congenital defects such as the absence, malfunction or retarded growth of the male internal genitalia. Some sexual problems can be helped by circumcision, when skin grows over the head of the penis restricting its ability to achieve an erection.

• Middle and old age: Menopause among women and similarly, andropause among men can lead to a slackening of interest in sex. Also, those above seventy years of age experience a distinct weakness in their semen production. Ill health, pain and reduced mobility can also cause difficulties in the sex act and lead to a loss of interest in sex. Loss of vital hormones in later life can also be a cause of lack of interest in sex and sexual debility.

• Decrease in the sperm count: Impotence of this kind could be due to poor diet which is cold, dry and made from incompatible recipes; nutritional, deficiency, zinc deficiency, suppression of hunger and exertion.

• Emotional problems: Impotence can also be borne out of constant exposure to debilitating physical or mental circumstances and anxieties, stress, mental tension, sorrow, bereavement or trauma; jealousy, anger of hyper-excitement. The loss of vitality and functional impotence cause severe immunodeficiency and even result in death.

• Illness: Ailments such as haemorrhoids, diabetes, heart disease and arthritis can have a negative impact on sexual performance. In women, lack and loss of sexual desire is known as frigidity and is also often caused by illness or discomfort. Vaginal dryness, pain during intercourse difficulty or vaginismus as well as orgasmic dysfunction are all problems relating to women.

Impotence

The word impotence is derived from the Latin *impotentia*, meaning 'lack of power'. It was first used to describe loss of sexual power in 1655 in, of all places; a treatise entitled *Church History of Britain* by Thomas Fuller.

Impotence is the failure to obtain or maintain an erection for the satisfactory achievement of heterosexual vaginal intercourse. It is usually taken to mean an adequate erection, of sufficient hardness, maintained for a sufficient length of time, which ends in an ejaculation that provides sexual fulfillment for both partners.

Impotence is a common and distressing condition that affects 10 to 30 per cent of men on a regular basis. All age groups are involved, but due to embarrassment or a mistaken belief that nothing can be done, victims often suffer in silence and despondency. Whatever the cause of impotence, 99 per cent of men can get their erections back by one of the many treatment options that are now available.

It is often assumed that impotence is a purely psychological problem, but in 40 per cent of cases a physical cause is involved. If a man awakes with a morning erection or can masturbate to orgasm when alone, the problem is more liable to be psychological rather than physical. If a male never manages an erection, even on waking, a physical problem is probable and this must be carefully looked into by a doctor specializing in urology.

During a night's sleep, between four and eight erections may occur naturally; unless there is a physical blockage to prevent them. A special device can be attached to the penis before going to sleep that regularly measures penile diameter and stiffness throughout the night. This is useful for differentiating between physical and psychological causes of impotence. Often, however, both physical and psychological factors play a role as a vicious circle builds up that causes anxiety and negative feelings to set in.

Physical Causes of Impotence

The most widespread physical cause of impotence is tiredness, overwork and stress. It is entirely common to perform under par in these circumstances. Other physical causes include drug side-effects, hardening of the arteries (atherosclerosis), leaking valves that stop blood pooling within spongy tissues, fibrosis, hormonal imbalances and nerve damage.

Atherosclerosis

Hardening and furring of the arteries is very common in late and middle age. Sometimes, the arteries leading to the penis become blocked and furred up with cholesterol deposits. This poor circulation means blood cannot flow easily into the penis in the volume required for a normal erection and impotence is the result.

There are tests that profile the blood flow into the penis (using dyes that show up on X-ray) and will show up any narrowing of the arteries that may be the cause of erectile failure. Ultrasound is also sometimes used to determine changes to the blood flow after injection with an erection-inducing drug.

Diabetes

Diabetes often causes impotence for two main reasons: it encourages furring up of the arteries (atherosclerosis) and, if not well controlled, can lead to lasting nerve damage from the high levels of circulating sugar crystals.

Drug Side-effects

Drug side-effects are a common and reversible cause of impotence. Among the prescription drugs, the worst offenders are beta-blockers - which work by damping down the activity of certain types of nerve. Beta-blockers are excellent drugs which are frequently prescribed to treat high blood pressure, angina, heart attacks, anxiety, palpitations, migraine, glaucoma and an over-active thyroid, but if this side-effect becomes troublesome it is important to tell your doctor so you can be switched to a different type of drug.

Thiazide diuretics (water tablets) prescribed to lower high blood pressure or reduce fluid accumulation in the body can also trigger erectile failure. Patients taking diuretics are twice as likely to be impotent as those on no drugs. Again, tell your doctor alternative treatments are available.

Anti-depressant tablets affect nerve endings in the nervous system and can also be at fault. If you are taking any drugs at all it is worth asking your doctor or a pharmacist whether these are likely to disturb your sex drive.

It is easy to forget that cigarette smoke contains a powerful drug, nicotine. Cigarette smoking is closely linked with erectile failure, and there is a clear dose-related effect: the more cigarettes smoked per day, the less rigid the erection. Cigarette smoking damages blood vessels and hastens 'furring up' of the arteries.

Fibrosis
If the blood supply is normal, fibrosis or a build-up of scar tissue (e.g. Peyronie's Disease) can make the penis rigid on one side only, rather than expansible. This stops the penis inflating fully, or makes it curve radically and painfully to one side. This can cause partial or total impotence. Surgical treatment to remove the scar tissue or to take a fold in the opposite side so that the erection becomes straight again, can help solve this problem.

Hormonal Imbalances
Sometimes a hormonal imbalance may be the cause of impotence, particularly if testosterone hormone levels are too low or prolactin hormone levels too high. If you suffer from impotence you should have blood tests to screen for hormonal problems. If an imbalance is found, this is generally easily treated.

Nerve Damage

Diseases or injuries to nerves can affect the nerves and can cause impotence. This includes men who suffer from acute multiple sclerosis, or who have sustained a spinal cord injury as a result, for example, of breaking their back or neck. Sometimes reflex erections can occur but ejaculation is not usually possible without some electrical stimulation.

Slow Leaks

In some males, erection starts off firmly and then slowly reduces due to a slow leak of blood out of the corpora cavernosa and corpus spongiosum. This is due to a weakness in the mechanism that compacts the outlet veins to prevent blood from draining away during an erection. This difficulty can be detected by special tests using dyes that show up on X-ray (cavernosometry). Venous leaks are a common cause of impotence in older men. Some men suffer from both poor blood supply and a venous leak.

The Treatment of Physical Impotence

The treatment of physical impotence is now sophisticated. Several options are available after full investigations have suggested the likely cause.

Oral Drugs

Many trials of an oral drug treatment for impotence are currently in progress. One drug, a derivative of yohimbine hydrochloride, from the African Pausinystalis yohimbe tree, has been proving very successful.

P.I.P.E.

Some patients are trained to give themselves an injection into the shaft of the penis. This is known as P.I.P.E - (Pharmacologically Induced Penile Erection). The injections are given by a very fine needle inserted into the corpora cavernosa. The shaft of the penis is not very pain-sensitive and the injections are not painful. After withdrawing the needle, the injection site is pressed firmly for 30 seconds so that no bleeding can occur. After an average of 8 minutes, an erection starts to develop as the arteries that supply blood to the penis dilate and the draining veins constrict.

The commonly used drug, papaverine, (priapism) can induce prolonged erections, but sometimes the penis needs to be drained of trapped blood to re-establish the circulation. Papaverine can also cause internal scarring and curvature (Peyronie's disease) in a few males. In the majority of cases, nevertheless, P.I.P.E. is very successful and has transformed the lives of many impotent males.

Another drug, prostaglandin E1, is prescribed instead of papaverine by some doctors as it has a lesser risk of side-effects.

A new development is a self-injection system known as Caverject (alprostadil). This works in a similar manner to prostaglandin E1 and can be prescribed by doctors. But some men have found it more painful than other drug treatments.

Surgical Implants

Prostheses are devices that can be surgically implanted into the penis to produce erection. There are two main types:

1. Semi-rigid rods giving the patient half an erection all of the time, this is not usually a problem and does not restrict urination.

2. Complicated, inflatable devices with small pumps implanted in the scrotum and a fluid reservoir bag implanted in the abdomen or pelvis. These devices are activated by squeezing the pump or activating a trigger button in the scrotum, reduction is achieved by pressing a release button.

Some semi-rigid implants have an implanted silver wire to make them flexible. The penis can then be turned and 'parked' when not in use. Newer designs consist of fixed, interlocking discs made of plastic. These can be rotated in one direction to lock and become rigid, then, after intercourse, rotated the other way to become flaccid. Insertion of an implant takes from two to three hours, depending on the type selected. The procedure is done under a local anaesthetic, or under a spinal epidural. (The body is then numb from the waist down; the same as many women experience during childbirth).

It takes about two weeks for the discomfort and swelling of the operation to settle, especially under the scrotum where the base of the penis is situated. Intercourse can then be resumed from four weeks subsequent to the operation; depending on the procedure used. The main risk with penile implantation is post-operative infection, but this seems to be quite rare. Ninety per cent of men with an implant are completely happy with its performance. Most implants are invisible, although the semi-rigid rods can make the penis stick out a little bit, but this does not look out of the ordinary.

Topical GTN

Glyceryl trinitrate (GTN) is a drug normally used to treat heart angina pains. GTN dilates blood vessels and increases blood flow. Research has found that GTN patches applied to the penis for one to two hours before intercourse can help to overcome impotence. The use of GTN patches has an advantage over GTN creams, as the latter are absorbed by vaginal tissues and can cause the side-effect of headaches in any female partners. You can get round this by using a condom.

Vacuum Erections

For a vacuum erection the penis is placed in a plastic tube from which air is extracted via a pump. The resultant vacuum makes the penis fill with blood and triggers an erection. Tthere is also some belief that it increases the size of the penis. A tight ring is then placed around the base of the penile shaft to trap the blood and maintain rigidity. The penis then stays erect once the vacuum cylinder is removed. Obviously, as it acts rather like a tourniquet, the penis appears rather blue, and the ring can only be left in place for a short while (otherwise the blood supply of the penis may be compromised). Another problem is that the elastic band stops semen emergence from the tip of the penis during ejaculation, so semen may seep out later, or may wash into the bladder to be urinated away; this is not harmful but does affect fertility.

Vascular Surgery

If there is a substantial blockage to penile blood inflow, it is feasible to have an operation, arterial by-pass graft, in which the blockage is by-passed using a length of your own vein, or synthetic tubing. Sometimes a single stricture can be dilated with a special balloon inserted into the artery under X-ray control, similar to some heart operations to clear clogged veins.

Another successful approach is to connect another artery, which normally delivers blood to the lower abdominal muscles, to the penis. This is joined to one of the penile arteries using a microsurgical technique. This procedure can instantly increase the blood flow to the penis and allow an erection to develop. Some of the penile-draining veins are generally tied off to increase the effect: this combines a better blood flow coming in with a weaker blood flow draining out. Success rates are often as high as 70 per cent.

Arterial by-pass surgery involves a fairly large incision that extends up the lower abdomen, but this usually requires a stay of several days in hospital.

If impotence is due solely to a slow venous leak, this is simply corrected by tying off the major veins draining the penis. This procedure is known as venous ligation, and is successful in 50 per cent of cases. Sometimes new veins will open up after the operation and venous leaking can return after a few years.

Psychological Causes of Impotence

Psychological problems account for up to 60 per cent of all cases of impotence. Counselling and psychotherapy are very helpful and often result in a dramatic improvement.

Psychological problems are usually based on fear, remorse, guilt or feelings of inadequacy and low self-esteem. The more a man worries about not getting an erection, the more the erection is likely to be unsuccessful. Thus it becomes a self-fulfilling forecast and compounds the problem. Relaxation training and professional psychosexual counselling are essential in these types of cases.

Psychosexual counselling often involves a temporary ban on penetrative sex. Sufferers are taught to relax with their partner while exploring each other's bodies afresh. Usually, it is agreed in advance that even if an erection is achieved, sexual penetration will not be attempted. (The man can please his partner in other ways but he should not be concerned with his own sexual pleasure or with his own erection or ejaculation.)

After several weeks of self-restraint, the couples are then allowed to try having sex with the female counterpart on top. This is known as the Mistress position. The so-called 'Missionary position' (man on top) is not good for men with semi-rigid erections.

A helpful and sympathetic partner is vitally important. He or she is an invaluable support during the investigation and treatment of the partner's impotence. A partner who mocks or ridicules (or even feels overly sorry for) a man's performance is making the problem worse and may even have contributed to it in the first place.

Premature Ejaculation

Premature ejaculation is the most common male sexual dysfunction. And there are three different ways of defining it:

1. If the man comes long before he wants to or before his partner requires him to.

2. If ejaculation occurs, ahead of time, before the penis penetrates the vagina.

3. If the man cannot stop himself ejaculating for at least one minute after penetrating his partner.

Most men experience premature ejaculation at some time during their lives, - most commonly when losing their virginity or when they are particularly nervous for some reason. It also occurs in over 50 per cent of males when making love to a new partner for the first time. Premature ejaculation is particularly common among teenagers and tends to become less of a problem for men in their twenties and thirties and beyond as they become more confident and controlled in their sexual encounters.

If a man can stop ejaculating for anything over one minute after penetration, this is normal. It may not sound very long, but our primitive male ancestors were originally designed to thrust only five or six times before reaching orgasm. Humans are unique among the animal kingdom in using sex for pleasure. The male chimpanzee, for example, ejaculates within 30 seconds of intercourse and the female satisfies herself by mating with as many males as she can find in quick succession.

Premature ejaculation is usually due to anxiety - especially if a new partner is involved. This often results in eagerness and over-excitement. The other main cause is anxiety about performance - whether you will be 'good enough' for your partner or will fail to satisfy. No man wants to feel his performance is not up to scratch. Most men brag about their sexual experience, but often they are not as confident in their prowess as they say.

Other causes of premature ejaculation are the man feeling that his partner is not really interested in sex, or if either partner has difficulty in showing or responding to affection.

Sometimes the opposite problem of retarded ejaculation occurs- especially if the male is trying to delay his orgasm to ensure his partner is fully satisfied.

The easiest way to make premature ejaculation less of a problem is to bring your partner to the point of orgasm during foreplay. Then, when your partner is about to come, penetration can occur or you can wait until after your partner's orgasm before entering. There are other techniques that help to overcome premature ejaculation. As some of these seem to take the pleasure out of sex, they will not suit every man:

• Wear a condom. This damps down sensory stimulation and usually helps to prolong intercourse.

• Use a local anaesthetic cream to numb the tip of the penis. These creams can be bought over the counter. Make sure you buy a pure anaesthetic cream rather than a preparation intended for piles, as the latter sometimes contains other agents that might cause irritation to both yourself and your partner.

• Tense the buttock muscles while thrusting; this helps to disguise signals from nerve endings in the penis and gives you something else to concentrate on.

• Think about something other than sex while making love, such as problems at work, or your plans for next years holiday. By taking your mind off sex (just for a minute!) you may find you can continue to penetrate your partner for longer.

• Just before ejaculation, the testicles naturally rise in the scrotum to sit close to the base of the penis. If you gently pull the testicles back down into the scrotum, you may find this helps delay ejaculation. You can also ask you partner to hold your balls during coitus, be careful not to twist them though.

• If you are able to penetrate your partner, pre-arrange a signal, such as saying 'cease'. Then, when you feel you are about to come, both you and your partner can remain very still and stop thrusting for a few seconds. This may help to prolong intercourse and can be repeated as often as necessary.

• The most well-known way of preventing premature ejaculation is the 'squeeze' technique. The man's partner gently masturbates him until he says he is about to come. The partner can then gently squeeze the penis between the thumb and two fingers just below the helmet, where the glands join the shaft. The squeeze ought to be firmly sustained for about five seconds and then the pressure relaxed for a minute.

This can be repeated to postpone ejaculation as often as you wish and is often extremely successful. By retraining your sexual habits, you will eventually be able to achieve normal intercourse. During intercourse, a man can also squeeze his penis himself, providing he has enough prior warning of impending ejaculation to reach down in time.

• After experiencing premature ejaculation, wait for an hour and then try again. The second erection frequently lasts much longer and orgasm can be delayed.

Retarded Ejaculation

Retarded ejaculation is the failure of a man to ejaculate, despite having prolonged intercourse, adequate stimulation, and a powerful desire to do so. This is an infrequent occurrence in a good number of men, especially when stressed or overly tired. But some males have never achieved ejaculation during sexual intercourse although most affected men are able to ejaculate during masturbation.

Medical conditions such as diabetes, an enlarged prostate gland, previous prostate operation or certain drugs (e.g. water tablets, tricyclic antidepressants, treatment for high blood pressure) are sometimes at fault. The commonest cause of ejaculatory failure, however, is psychological inhibitions such as in the case of:

• Newlyweds sleeping next door to their parents, close to other people or children.

• Discovering a spouse or partner is unfaithful.

• While having sex with a bored or uninterested partner.

• A recent condom breaks when pregnancy would have been devastating.

• Having recently been interrupted during sex, such as by your children.

• A man who is struggling with his sexual orientation may have trouble achieving ejaculation.

Where possible make sure your environment is compatible with unstressful sex - that is, quiet, with no risk of interruption or being overheard, restful and comfortable. If problems persist you can be referred for psychotherapy, which will involve a structured programme.

Female Sexual Problems

If you are a woman experiencing problems with sex, you are not alone. Recent studies reveal that almost 40 percent of women of all ages report having sexual problems at some time in their life.

What Causes Female Sexual Problems?

Sexual problems can be influenced by a wide variety of reasons. There are two main components; biological and psychological and usually they interact. Biological difficulties usually involve such things as hormonal imbalances, infections (like yeast infections), or diseases (like diabetes or multiple sclerosis) that have potential side effects like pain during sex or excessive dryness.

There are also specific times in a woman's life when she is more susceptible to sexual problems because of hormonal changes. For example, some women experience a range of sexual responses right after childbirth and during menopause. Also, some commonly prescribed medications, like certain antidepressants, can lead to sexual side effects. There is also the psychological aspect. This can include such things as the many conflicting cultural messages one learns about sexuality. Gender messages are especially influential, impacting how a woman views her sexual self, including body image, role in society, sexual-self power, parenthood (or fear of being a parent) and her view of her partner.

From birth throughout her life every woman is developing a unique 'sexual narrative' influenced by culture, religion, gender, family of origin, and personal experiences. This 'narrative' takes on the beliefs and meanings that she attributes to her sexuality. All couples must negotiate their personal 'sexual narrative' as they cultivate their own approach to sexual communication and activity together. This should be a continuing process, since everyday life problems may get in the way of intimacy and sexuality. Job worries, pressures of juggling work and family, fear of pregnancy, substance abuse, depression, and financial worries can all influence how you feel sexually. In this modern world, we all have a lot on our mind that can get in the way even when you want to focus on being intimate with your partner.

Over time, psychological difficulty can lead to biological problems and vice versa. It all starts to mist together so you can't even really identify where the issues started. You just know you need to get help.

Reasons for Female Sexual Dysfunction

• Hypoactive sexual desire disorder is characterized by an absence of libido. There is no interest in initiating sex and little desire to seek stimulation. Sexual aversion disorder is characterized by an aversion to or avoidance or dismissal of sexual prompts or sexual contact. It may be acquired following sexual or physical abuse and or trauma and may be life-long. The main feature of female sexual arousal disorder is an inability to achieve and progress through the stages of 'normal' female arousal. Female orgasmic disorder is defined as the delay or absence of orgasm after 'normal' arousal.

• Dyspareunia is marked by genital pain before, during, or after intercourse.

• Vaginismus is the involuntary contraction of the perineal muscles around the vagina as a response to attempted penetration. Contraction makes vaginal penetration difficult or impossible.

These disorders must cause personal distress and must not be accounted for by a medical condition. A distinction is made between disorders that are life-long and those that are acquired, as well as those that are situational and generalized.

Medical

In cases where a medical condition is suspected as the underlying cause, whether it causes inadequate blood flow, nerve-related loss of sensitivity, or reduced hormone levels, a specialist conducts an appropriate diagnosis. Sexual problems may be symptomatic of diseases that require treatment, like diabetes, endocrine disorders of the hypothalamic-pituitary-gonadal axis, and neurological disorders.

The American Foundation of Urologic Disease (AFUD) classifies the APA's criteria into these four types of disorder:

• Hypoactive sexual desire disorder; includes sexual aversion disorder

• Sexual arousal disorder

• Orgasmic disorder

• Sexual pain disorders; includes vaginismus, dyspareunia

Contrary to APA stipulation, dyspareunia (pain during intercourse) may be diagnosed as a result of inadequate vaginal lubrication, which may be considered an arousal disorder and treated as such. Pain is associated with recurrent medical conditions, including cystitis.

Physiological Diagnostic Tests

Vaginal blood flow and engorgement (pooling and swelling of vaginal tissue) can be measured with vaginal photoplethysmography, in which an acrylic tampon-shaped instrument inserted in the vagina uses reflected light to sense flow and temperature. It cannot be used to assess advanced levels of arousal, say, during orgasm, because movement skews its reading. Also, limited knowledge of normative vaginal engorgement levels makes for only speculative results. Vaginal pH testing, commonly performed by gynaecologists and urologists to detect bacteria-causing vaginitis, may be useful. A probe inserted into the vagina takes the reading. Decreasing hormone levels and diminished vaginal secretion associated with menopause cause a rise in pH (over 5), which is easily detected with the test. A biothesiometer, a small cylindrical instrument, may be used to assess the sensitivity of the clitoris and labia to pressure and temperature. Readings are taken before and after the subject watches erotic videos and masturbates with a vibrator for approximately 15 minutes.

Treatment

There are three primary types of experimental treatment for female sexual dysfunction:

1. Education on female anatomy, arousal, and response; where blood flow, hormone levels, and sexual anatomy are normal.
Educating both women and men on how to talk about and respond to a woman's psychological and physical stimulatory needs can only happen if both partners recognize that there is a problem. Behavioural and sex therapists note the need for partners to examine the actual act of having sex, including foreplay, intercourse, and talking about sex. Sex therapists and psychologists may assist in improving communication between partners.

2. Hormone replacement therapy (including treatment of the underlying disorder)
Hormone replacement therapy (HRT) is aimed at restoring hormone levels affected by age, surgery, or hormone dysfunction to normal, thus restoring sexual function. Estrogen and testosterone levels are measured and treated by endocrinologists.

3. Vascular treatment (including treatment of the underlying disorder)
Ayurveda
Ayurvedic texts have devoted whole sections to therapies with include the use of drugs, diet and regimen essential for sexually fulfilling that harmonious lifestyle. The Charaka Samhita is a supreme example of such a text which provides an insight into the importance of sexual activity and the place it had in ancient Indian thought. Depending on the times and sociological conditions prevailing, emphasis is given to

the two major aspects of sex 'procreation' and 'enjoyment or pleasure'. Manu the stern law giver, stressed "procreation the goal"; the sage Vatsyayana in his immortal classic, The *Kama Sutra*, showed greater concern for the enjoyment and pleasure derived from sex by both partners. Both however, looked upon sexual activity as very important in fulfilling the life of any individual.

In Ayurvedic medicine, Vajikarana is the science of aphrodisiacs, a medical intervention in the form of Rasayan and Vajikaran, therapies function as an aid towards sexual fulfilment. Rasayan is a rejuvenating and nourishing therapy which involves the observance of a strict diet and self-imposed discipline as regards the practice of sex. The body and the mind are cleansed thoroughly during this vigorously administered therapy so as to make the individual receptive for the Vajikarana or aphrodisiac therapy which is to follow.

Often, after an Indian wedding, the bridal chamber is decorated with flowers and the fragrance of flowers and incense fills the air. Sweets made especially for the occasion are kept by the bedside along with a jar of warm milk. Milk according to Ayurveda is an excellent vitalizer and should be taken before and after sexual activity. Milk plays an important role in aphrodisiac or Vajikarana therapy.

For sexual dysfunction, be it male or female, communication is the key, talk to your partner, talk to your doctor and get the right help. You may need to look at your medication, use lubrication or in the case of psychological stresses, talk to a professional counsellor or sex therapist. Find out what is causing the problem and deal with it appropriately.

Chapter 5

The Human Body

The human body is a wondrous mechanism, it can be the agent of pleasure and pain and fantastic athletic ability. It is the agent of great pleasure and is as sensitive and responsive as a barometer. We all take our bodies for granted and it is only when they fail us that we appreciate just how amazing they are. Love your body, nourish and pamper it and know its secrets and sexual signals.

Armpits and Perspiration

Our armpit is known as the axilla; this small hairy zone plays a very important role in chemical signalling and reflects a major changing in the sexual habit of the human species.

Females possess more scent glands than males and the odours produced differ between the sexes, suggesting that they operate as sexual signals between amorous partners. Recent experiments have shown that blindfolded men become more sexually aroused by sniffing female armpit sweat then by smelling expensive commercial perfumes.

These armpit scent glands are called apocrine glands and their secretions are slightly oilier than ordinary sweat. They do not develop until puberty, when the arrival of sex hormones activates them and at the same time causes the growth of armpit hair. The hair acts as a scent trap, keeping the glandular secretions within the axillary region and helping to intensify their signal. There is an old English folk custom, handed down from generation to generation, based on the idea that if a young man wishes to seduce a young woman at a dance he must place a clean handkerchief in his armpit, beneath his shirt, before starting to dance. Afterwards he takes it out and fans her with it as if trying to cool her. In fact what he is doing is wafting his apocrine scent over her in the hope that she will be seduced by its fragrance.

In rural Austria the trick worked the other way, young women would place a slice of apple in their armpits when dancing and when the music stopped, they would offer it to their favoured male partner to eat, when he consumed it have been automatically exposed to her personal sexual fragrance. This trick was also known in Elizabethan England, where a whole, peeled apple, known as a 'love apple', was placed in the young woman's armpit until is was soaked with her sweat, then she would give it to her sweetheart who would inhale its fragrance.

Later, in the 16th century, the sexual impact of female armpit's fragrance is said to have made itself felt at the French court. A beautiful young princess, Mary of Cleves, the wife of the ugly Prince of Condé, was feeling hot from vigorous dancing at court, and retired to change her sweat stained chemise in one of the side rooms, adjoining the Louvre ballroom. The Duc d'Anuou, soon to be King Henri 11 of France, also suffering from the heat, entered this side room and thinking the discarded chemise was a napkin, used to wipe his perspiring face. According to the chronicler of the time, his senses were deeply affected by this action. Already a secret admirer of the teenage princess, from the moment he inhaled her fragrance he developed an uncontrollable passion for her and was forced to break his silence and tell her of his desire for her. But the union was not to be and caused him years of frustration and heartbreak.

Considering the major industry that today is based on the sale of underarm deodourant and vaginal deodorizers, these stories sound rather odd. If human beings carry such a powerful sexual stimulus under their arms and in the sweat glands why do so many of us go to such trouble to remove it with washing, rubbing and spraying and in the case of many women and some men depilation? The answer has to do with clothing; the young men in the English folk tales were scrubbed and wearing their best clean shirt to the dance, and produced fresh apocrine secretion from their scent glands. Soaked in these, a clean handkerchief really does carry a strongly sexual scent signal; this is the primeval system at work. Sadly today with our bodies covered in layers of clothes our sweaty skin can easily become a hothouse where millions of bacteria start to decay, and lead to today's dread of body odour.

As long ago as the first century BCE, the Roman poet Ovid, in his handbook on seduction, *The Art of Love*, warned the ladies that "they carry a goat in their armpits". More recent research has shown that the armpit secretions of males and females differs chemically in several ways and have odour appeal specifically directed at the opposite sex. The male secretion is said to be muskier, with the male hormone androstrerone playing a significant role. However in its pure fresh form neither male nor female secretion is easily detected consciously by the human nose. These appear to act at an unconscious level, leaving us feeling stimulated but not knowing why.

Orientals, incidentally, lack this underarm odour signalling system almost entirely. Among the Koreans at least half the population have no axillary scent glands and the glands are also rare among Japanese, with 90 per cent of the population having no detectable underarm odour. In fact those having strong smelling armpits in Japan are considered to have a disease and have been given the clinical name or 'osmidrosis azillae'. At one time individuals suffering from this ailment were even excused military service. In China the situation is even more extreme, with only 2-3 percent of the population having any detectable armpit odour. Because of this racial difference Orientals often find the natural armpit odour of European and Africans overpowering and even offensive.

The removal of armpit hair by shaving, waxing and creaming, is a comparatively recent practice first introduced in the western world in the 1920s by the newly burgeoning cosmetic industry. Occasionally there has been a small rebellion against this popular form of armpit despoilment. The famous lover guide, *The Joy of Sex*, published in 1972 was strongly opposed to depilation believing the armpit to be areas for caressing and kissing and should not be shaved. The closing year of the twentieth century saw the arrival of a magazine called *Hair to Stay*, subtitled the world's only magazine for lovers of natural hairy women. Women in the late 20th century who chose not to shave their underarms were categorized, ridiculed and embarrassed. These women were considered to be lesbians, radical feminists, immigrants who don't know better, or hippies left over from the 60s. This is wrong, the magazine insisted, because from a psychological social point of view, the act of removing body hair is a rebellion against sexuality. Underarm hair it claimed acts as a transmitting antennas, sent out signals to invite sexual intercourse. Warming to its theme it went on to say that when an adult woman shows off hairless armpit she is symbolically offering herself as a child and is therefore encouraging a perverted attitude to sex. It conveniently failed to point out that this extreme line of argument would end up accusing every clean shaven adult male of encouraging paedophilia, because little boys don't have beards.

Genitals

Female
The female genitals, the outer labia and inner labia, become engorged with blood and swell to twice its normal size and develop a greatly increased sensitivity when she is aroused. The mount of Venus also known by its Latin name of *mons veneris*, and sometimes called the mons pubis is a sturdy pad of fatty tissue, covered in pubic hair, that acts as a buffer for the pubic bone. It is situated just above the labia and its role is to protect the pubic bone from the impact of the male body during intercourse. This is a sensitive area and should be massaged in foreplay. Some women can achieve orgasm simply by massaging this area. The mount of Venus does not appear until puberty when hormonal changes transform a woman's adult shape.

The inner labia, also known as the labia minora, meaning 'little lips', or the mymphaea is positioned inside the fleshy outer labia and are a pair of sensitive flaps that are hairless, and highly sensitive. During pelvic thrusting these inner labia receive such prolonged tactile stimulation from the erect penis that they become swollen and suffused with blood turning red. These inner lips vary greatly in shape and size. Among the Bushmen people of Southern Africa the labia minora are sometimes greatly elongated and hang down between the legs. They have been known to measure up to 11 cm (4.5 inches), and can be tucked into the vagina. Today in the era of the 'body perfect' cosmetic surgeons can do genital enhancement and can reduce the size of the inner labia or do an operation to have their symmetry restored, Labioplasty, as this is called, has become the most commonly requested form of what is now known as 'intimate surgery'.

The vagina is a passage of about 8-10 cm (3-4 inches) long when not in a state of arousal. In virgins there is a thin membrane of skin, like a collar partially closing the entrance to the vagina. This hymen or maidenhead, has been of extreme importance historically in cultures where bridegrooms have demanded untouched or virgin brides. Traditionally the skin is torn by the first insertion of the male penis on the wedding night and there is then bleeding. In some cultures a bloody bed sheet had to be displayed the next morning as proof of a virgin bride.

Inside the vagina there are two zones of unusual sensitivity, or 'hot spots'. These are small zones of heightened erotic sensitivity, the stimulation of which during the mating act helps to bring the female nearer to an orgasmic condition. The female zones of sensitivity are: the clitoris, the U-spot and the G-spot and the A-spot. The first two are outside the vagina the second two are inside it.

• The clitoris is the best known of the female genital hot spots, located at the top of the vulva, where the inner labia joins at the upper end. It is visible as a small nipple sized protuberance and is covered by a protective hood. It is a bundle of 8,000 nerve fibres and is very sensitive. It becomes enlarged and swollen during copulation and during foreplay. Many women can reach orgasm purely from clitoral stimulation. Clitoral vibrators are the most commonly sold sex aid. The clitoris is like an iceberg - it has a larger part hidden beneath the surface and during intercourse this hidden clitoral shaft is massaged by the male organ. The clitoris is well worth taking time over, orally or mechanically, or during intercourse as it is the stimulation of the clitoris that will most likely lead to the female orgasm.

• The U-spot is a small patch of sensitive erectile tissue located just above the on either side of the urethral opening. Less well known than the clitoris its erotic potential was only recently investigated by American clinical research workers. They found that if this region was gently caressed with the finger, the tongue or the tip of the penis there was an unexpectedly powerful erotic response.

• The G-spot or Grafenberg spot is a small highly sensitive area located 5-8 cm (2-3 inches) inside the vagina, on the front or upper wall. Named after its discoverer a German gynaecologist called Ernst Grafenberg; it is sometime romantically referred to as the Goddess Spot. The G-spot is a small patch of vaginal wall protruding into the vaginal canal that becomes raised during intercourse; but not in the 'missionary position'. Grafenberg called it 'an erotic zone'. It is not a sex button but it is a sensitive patch that can heighten sexual response.

• The A-spot, AFE-zone or Anterior Fronix Erogenous Zone. Also referred to as the Epicentre, this is patch of sensitive tissue at the inner end of the vaginal tube between the cervix and the bladder, described technically as the 'female degenerated prostrate'. Direct stimulation of this spot can produce violent orgasmic contractions. Unlike the clitoris it is not supposed to suffer from post orgasmic over sensitivity. Its existence was reported by a Malaysian physician in Kuala Lumpur as recently as the 1990's. It is positioned just above the cervix at the innermost point of the vaginal canal. Pressure on it produces rapid lubrication of the vagina, even in women who are not normally very sexually responsive. It is now possible to buy a special AFE vibrator long thin and upwardly curved to probe this area.

The vagina becomes looser with age and after childbirth and it is now possible to have an operation to tighten it. Today there is a trend for studs and rings inserted in the vulva and sometimes even the clitoris.

The time taken for a woman to reach orgasm can be as little as 5 minutes but the average time, based on a study of 20,000 female orgasms, proved to be about 20 minutes. Following an orgasm, the clitoris, labia vagina and uterus all return to their normal relaxed condition. Some women find it possible to enjoy multiple orgasms one after another in quick succession, while others experience such an intense first climax that they do not want to repeat the experience for a time.

Female Circumcision

Over history and even today and in many cultures the female genitals have been the victim of an amazing variety of mutilation and restriction. For organs that are capable of giving so much pleasure they have been given an inordinate amount of pain.

The most common form of defacement has been circumcision. This mutilation has been rare in the West, although as recently as 1937 a Texas doctor was advocating the removal of the clitoris to cure frigidity. In many parts of Africa, the Middle East and Asia female circumcision has been common and widespread for centuries and it is still going on today in as many as 20 countries in the world. Some of the reasons for this operation include: if a man's penis touches a woman's clitoris, he may become sick, may become impotent, or he may die. If a baby touches its mother's clitoris when it is being born it may die or be deformed. Possessing a clitoris makes a mother's milk poisonous. Possessing external genitals makes women smell evil. It may also drive a husband to take illegal drugs when trying to match his wife's insatiable sexual urges. Removing external genital prevents a wide range of women's ailments, including; a yellow complexion, nervousness, ugliness, neurosis and vaginal cancer. The true reason is that by reducing women's sexual pleasure it helps to subordinate them to their tyrannical male partners in a male dominated society.

In the worst cases young girls have had their labia and clitoris scraped or cut away and their vaginal opening stitched up with silk, catgut or thorns, leaving only a tiny opening for urine and menstrual blood. After the operation the girls' legs are bound together to ensure that scar tissue forms and that the condition becomes permanent. Later when they are married these women suffer the pain of having the binding removed and being broken by their husbands. If the husband went away for a long trip the wife could be sewn up again while he was away.

This extreme form of genital mutilation infibulations is sometimes called Pharaonic circumcision. And the procedure that only removes the clitoris and labia is referred to as Sunna circumcision, because it is claimed to have been recommended by the prophet Mohammed, this only requires the tip of the clitoris to be cut away.

There are as many as 2 million girls that have to suffer from female circumcision every year, and it is possible that over 100 million women alive today have been mutilated in this way.

Male

The human penis is the biggest of any existing primate and, unlike the males of many species (e.g. whale, bear, walrus, cattle, bats, rodents and lower monkeys) it has evolved without the need for a strengthening bone. It is an amazing example of bio-engineering, based on three inflatable cylinders of erectile tissue: two larger corpora cavernosa (cavernous bodies) on the upper surface and the thinner corpus spongiosum (spongy body) running centrally up the underside.

On the upper (dorsal) side of the penis, a dorsal vein drains blood away from the organ; two dorsal arteries, which supply blood to the skin, pulsate where the penis joins the lower abdomen. Several superficial veins are also visible, which drain the skin and glands of the penis, but not the deeper erectile tissues.

The single corpus spongiosum contains the urethra, the tube through which urine flows from the bladder and out. At the tip of the penis the corpus spongiosum expands to form the bulky 'helmet' or glands. At the base, behind the scrotum, the corpus spongiosum thickens again to form the root or bulb of the penis. This is attached to a thick fibrous membrane for stability and is surrounded by a muscle (bulbospongiosus) that contracts rhythmically during ejaculation). The corpus spongiosum also contains erectile tissue that swells in a similar manner to the corpora cavernosa for the period of an erection.

The male phallus has appeared in art and in worship throughout history. In the Elephanta caves on an island in the Arabian Sea off the coast of

Bombay, India is a spectacular sight. These temple-like caves contain a huge representation of the great phallus of the Indian god Shiva, the creator and destroyer of the world. Illuminated by thousand of candles it is visited my thousands of pilgrims day and night. The ancient Greeks had a god, Priapus, whose phallus was so huge that he had to carry it in a wheelbarrow. The Egyptians honoured the god Osiris in the form of the djed pillar.

The Japanese have a traditional dance with huge artificial phalluses that is used in their traditional fertility festival which is intended to evoke the creative powers of nature.

The erect penis is of course a sexual symbol, but it is also a symbol of the life force itself and for ancient peoples, blood was also the carrier of spiritual energy and the soul. (See references to the male phallus in the chapter on Mayday)

History of Male Circumcision
The tradition of male genital mutilation is far older than recorded history. It seems to have originated in Eastern Africa long before this time. Circumcision is still widely practiced in many countries in Africa as part of the rite to manhood ceremony. Numerous theories have been put forward to explain the origin of genital mutilation. One theory postulates that circumcision began as a way of 'purifying' individuals and society by reducing sexuality and sexual pleasure. Human sexuality was seen as dirty or impure in some societies; hence cutting off the pleasure-producing parts was the obvious way to 'purify' someone.

It is now known that the male foreskin, or prepuce, is the principal location of erogenous sensation in the human male. Removal of the prepuce is believed to significantly reduce erogenous sensation. Therefore circumcision is revealed as a sacrifice of 'sinful' human enjoyment.

Jews adopted circumcision as a religious ritual and preserved this prehistoric practice into modern times. The circumcision of Abraham removed only the very tip that extended beyond the glands penis.

Moses and his sons were not circumcised. It is worthy of note that after the Israelites were circumcised, they immediately became soldiers in Joshua's army for the conquest of Palestine. In contrast to the Jews, the Greeks and the Romans placed a high value on the prepuce. The Romans passed several laws to protect the prepuce by prohibiting circumcision.

Much later in the Hellenic period, about 140 C.E., the circumcision procedure was modified to make it impossible for a Jew to appear to be an uncircumcised Greek. A sweeping new procedure called peri'ah was introduced by the priests and rabbis. In this procedure the foreskin was stripped away from the gland, with which it is fused in the infant. In a painful procedure known today as a synechotomy, more foreskins were removed than before and the injury was also far greater. With the introduction of peri'ah, the gland could not easily be recovered, and so no Jewish male would easily be able to appear as an uncircumcised Greek. It may have been at this time that the Pondus Judaeus, also known as Judaeum Pondum, a bronze weight worn by Jews on the residual foreskin to stretch it back into a foreskin, gained popularity amongst Jewish males. This lessened the ugly appearance of the bare exposed circumcised penis. This restorative procedure was known by the Greek word *epispasm*, or 'rolling inward.'

The third stage of ritual circumcision, the Messisa or Metzitzah, was not introduced until the Talmudic period (500-625 C.E). In Metzitzah, the mohel a ritual circumciser sucks blood from the penis of the circumcised infant with his mouth. This procedure has been responsible for the death of many Jewish babies due to infection. In modern times, a glass tube is sometimes used instead. The Reform movement within Judaism considered circumcision to be a cruel practice. The Reform movement at Frankfort declared in 1843 that circumcision was not necessary.

Christians took a strong stand against circumcision in the 1st century and rejected circumcision at the Council at Jerusalem. St. Paul, the apostle to the gentiles, taught parents not to circumcise their children. In a reference to the old practices of genital mutilation, St. Paul warned Titus to "beware of the circumcision group".

70

The modern use of Hebrew circumcision as a medical practice dates from about 1865 in England and about 1870 in the USA. The procedure accepted for medical use essentially was the Jewish peri'ah. Moscucci reports that circumcision was imposed in an attempt to prevent masturbation. No scientific studies were carried out to determine the efficacy and safety of circumcision prior to its introduction into medical practice, nor were any studies conducted to determine the social effects of imposing genital alteration surgery on a large portion of the population.

South Koreans started to circumcise children during the American trusteeship following World War II. The American cultural practice of circumcision became nearly universal in South Korea after the Korean War of 1950-52. In 1949, Gairdner wrote that circumcision was medically unnecessary and non-beneficial. The British National Health Service (NHS) deleted non-therapeutic neonatal circumcision from the schedule of covered procedures in 1950. After publication of this article the procedure was not practiced by the NHS.

America waited another 20 years before addressing the problem of non-therapeutic circumcision. The *Journal of the American Medical Association* published an influential by Dr. E. Noel Preston, Captain, MC, and USAF. Dr. Preston established that there is no therapeutic or prophylactic benefit to circumcision. He also cited "undesirable psychological, sexual, and medico-legal difficulties." The incidence of male neonatal circumcision in the U.S. peaked in 1971 and began a slow decline that continues to the present.

Today circumcision is practiced for health and cleanliness reasons, many men find the exposed head more sensitive and prefer it to the covered head of an un-circumcised penis. Also a lot of women prefer a circumcised penis, finding it aesthetically pleasing, cleaner and more pleasant to kiss and play with.

Pubic Hair

In childhood our bodies are hairless but at the approach of puberty our bodies change with the increase of hormone production. Girls start to grow breasts and boys' genitals develop and their sex drive goes into overdrive and both male and female start to develop hair on their bodies. Many young girls can be quite upset by this sudden growth of pubic hair. Throughout history public hair has been denied and censored, airbrushed and omitted from art and sculpture

In different parts of the world, there is a considerable variation in the type of female public hair, from short to long, from sparse to dense, from straight and soft, to coarse and curly. Also in colour and texture, the pubic hair does not always match the head hair. Many dark haired women have lighter pubic hair, often with a red tint. Most women have wavy or curly public hair, even when their head hair is straight. The main exception to this is found in the Far East, where the straight black head hair is matched by pubic hair that is short straight, not thick but rather sparse, forming a somewhat narrow triangle.

Why do we have Pubic Hair?

• Firstly, the display of pubic hair is visual and primeval and in naked times it would act as a signal indicating the person is now a sexual adult, and to the prehistoric male the presence of visible pubic hair would have helped to trigger his sexual response, while its absence would have inhibited it. It is curious that this inhibition is lacking in paedophiles.

• Secondly, the function of pubic hair is to act as a scent trap, skin glands in the genital region secret special pheromones, natural scent that adult males unconsciously find sexually attractive the hair at the genital region traps this scent.

• Thirdly, the pubic hair is there for protection for the genital region and the sensitive tender skin and membranes of the area. Pubic hair could also be considered a modesty veil to the vulnerable female genitals and protect it from cold and accidents.

A German anthropologist observed, while visiting the tribal people of the Bismarck Archipelago in the South Pacific, that the women wiped their hands on their pubic hair to dry them as we would use a towel.

As with many other parts of the female body the pubic region has often been modified, this has involved dying, shaping, decorating, or removing pubic hair. Early feminists saw 'pubic hair dressing' as pandering to males and rejected the idea, along with other forms of makeup or cosmetic improvement. Hedonists, in contrast, see the natural condition of the pubic hair as appealingly erotic.

The removal of pubic hair gives rise to two completely contradictory reactions, puritanical support comes from the idea that public hair is potentially dirty or smelly, and that its removal is therefore hygienic and cleansing. In addition the idea of being completely smooth and childlike and is non erotic. In the past, many female statues had smooth pubic regions with no hint of hair or any other genital features. It has also led to artist models shaving off their pubic hair, ostensibly to clarify the details of their pelvic contours, but in reality to make them look more like sanitized classical statues.

There is one famous story of the Victorian scholar John Ruskin, who was a British professor of art, when he was 28 he met his future wife but he knew nothing of sexual matters. They married and he was stunned to discover that she had hair around her genitals. He had only seen the statues of classic sculpture and knew the female form as smooth and hairless. He was never able to have sex with his wife and the marriage was later annulled on the grounds that it was never consummated, after his wife was medically examined and found to still be a virgin.

The sexual appeal of pubic hair removal has many sources:

• The first is that removal of pubic hair lays bare the genital slit. It allows closer contact and for many men a more visual excitement and comfort especially in the act of cunnilingus.

• Secondly, the hairless condition transmits a signal of virginal innocence, the Lolita look, or schoolgirl fantasy which does appeal to many men.

In history the removal of female pubic hair is far from being a modern fashion. Records show that it can be traced back as far as the ancient Egyptian. Egyptian women were very fastidious about the body hair, and removed all trace of it with wax or a cream, made of honey and oil. King Solomon was said to dislike female pubic hair and when the Queen of Sheba visited him, in the tenth century BCE, he asked her to depilate herself before making love, requiring that she make herself open to him by removing 'nature's veil'.

Later in history in Ancient Greece it is recorded that men preferred their women to remove the hairs from their privy parts, this was because the strong growth of hair in southern women would otherwise prevent their private parts from being seen.

Some of the methods for female depilation were; hair by hair plucking, singeing with a burning lamp, and another was singeing with hot ashes.

The practice of female pubic hair removal was also popular in Ancient Rome, but the techniques were slightly different. Like the Greeks they did employ plucking, using special tweezers called volsella, but unlike the Greeks they replaced the dangerous technique of singeing with the application of depilatory creams and waxing with pitch or resin. Fashionable Roman young girls would start to use one of these methods as soon as their pubic hairs began to grow.

When the crusaders were in the Holy Land they discovered that Arab women depilated the pubic region, and, impressed by what they experienced, they brought the fashion back with them to Europe where some aristocrats adopted it during the Middle Ages.

Later in the 16th Century it is known that Turkish women had special rooms that were set aside in the public baths just for hair depilation. It was thought to be sinful for them to allow their pubic hair to grow naturally.

In Victorian Europe the removal of pubic hair was unheard of except possibly among the professional ladies of the night. It did not become popular again until the sexually liberated 1960's.

During the 1970's the rise of the feminist movement saw a return to the natural look and a full pubic bush was again in fashion. But by the end of the 20th century a new trend began because of the skimpy nature of swimsuits. Waxing became the norm, most women had their public hair trimmed or narrowed and some had it shaped. In the 21st century you can have a bewildering range of styles, shapes and patterns, from a heart to an arrow or thunderbolt.

A complete contrast to pubic hair reductions is the curious custom of merkin wearing. A merkin is a pubic wig made of human hair, nylon or yak belly hair. It is held in place either by an inconspicuous G-string or by gluing it on to the real pubic hair beneath.

Merkins have a long history, stretching back hundreds of years and are still offered for sale today. Their original function, centuries ago, was to hide the ravages of syphilis or other venereal diseases that disfigured the external genitals. Later, they were used by prostitutes for customers who found a generous 'bush' pubic patch sexually appealing. More recently in the world of film making they have been used as a modesty mask by actresses who were required to appear naked.

Some merkins have been decorated with jewels, flowers, or coloured ribbons and all three of these types of pubic embellishment have been known for centuries, both on merkins and occasionally even on real pubic hair. There are records that prove they were popular as long ago as the 16th century. The murdered body of a French marchioness was left in the public street with her genital area deliberately exposed, there for all to see was her pubic hair adorned with crimped ribbons of different colours. It seems that when the King of France insisted that the ladies of the royal court should restrict the splendour of their costumes, they obeyed the monarch, but then compensated for this imposition by taking their fashionable fripperies underground.

Diana the many-breasted goddess.
From the fountain of Diana Efesia in the Tivoli Gardens

Breasts

Breasts have received more erotic attention from males that any other part of the female body. The breasts of a human woman have two biological functions, one parental and the other sexual. The areolar surrounding the nipple is an intriguing anatomical detail of the human species. In virgin females and those who have yet to become mothers it is a pinkish colour but during pregnancy it changes. About two months after conception it starts to grow larger and become darker. By the time lactation has started it is often a dark brown and when the baby is weaned the colour never quite goes back to original pink.

At times the atmosphere, and religion, of society has demanded that the sexuality of the female bust be suppressed, puritans achieved this by forcing young women to wear tight bodices that flattened their breasts and gave an innocent childlike shape even to mature adults. In 17th century Spain young ladies suffered even greater ignominy, having their swelling breasts flattened by lead plates that were pressed tightly on to their chest in an attempt to prevent nature from taking its normal physical course. Such cruel imposition only highlights the length some societies will go to subjugate the freedom of the sexual animal that is woman.

A woman's breasts play an important part in foreplay; the male will kiss and suck the nipples and caress the breasts with his hands. The area around the nipples contains apocrine glands that transmit scent signals to the male nose. Apocrine glands are the ones responsible for the especial sexual fragrances of the armpits and genital region and although the males are not consciously aware of the erotic odour from these glands their secretion does make an unconscious impact on sexual arousal. As sexual arousal heightens, the female breast undergoes several marked changes; the nipples become erect, increasing in length by up to a centimetre. The breasts themselves become engorged with blood, increasing in size by up to 25 per cent, they also become more sensitive and responsive to the touch.

On the approach of orgasm two further changes occur, the areolar patches becomes tumescent and swell so much that they start to mask the nipple, there also appears a strange measles like rash over the surface of the breast and chest. This 'sex flush' occurs in some 75 per cent of women, a similar effect to the nervous flush that some people will exhibit when under stress.

The breasts have also been used as a substitute to the vagina when the woman is menstruating, if her breasts are large enough, the male can place his penis between the breasts and rub himself off to climax.

About one in every 200 women has more than two breasts, a condition referred to as polymastiia. Very occasionally a woman is found who does have more than two functional, milk producing breasts. A most extraordinary case concerned a French woman in 1886 who had five pairs of fully functioning breasts. A few months later a Polish woman was found who also had ten functional breasts. These extra breasts are remains of our ancient ancestry.

Several famous women have possessed more that two breasts, Julia, the mother of the Roman emperor Alexander Severus, was many breasted and was given the name Julia Mamaea as a result. More surprisingly, close examination reveals that the famous statue of the Venus de Milo, in the Louvers, displays three breasts. The wife of King Henry V111, Ann Boleyn, was also said to possess a third breast. Witches were once believed to have extra nipples with which they suckled their familiars, and women who were thought to be guilty of witchcraft were searched for telltale signs of their evil ways. The most famous multi breasted figure in history is the Diana or Artemis, of Ephesus. Her ample sculptured bosom displays several rows of breasts crowded together, and some ancient art and statues in India also display the multiple breasted goddess...

In most cultures it is frowned upon to expose naked breasts in public, even the harmless breast feeding mother was once considered brazen and unnatural in public, thank heavens attitudes have changed in the last few years. But there was once a time in Venice when bare breasts had to be exposed, by law, this was to prove that the prostitutes were female and not male. They would sit on a bridge which became so famous that it was named the Ponte delle Tette, 'Bridge of Breasts'.

78

The Buttocks

The Greeks worshipped the human bottom and saw them as supremely human, as non bestial. The curvaceous Goddess of Love, Aphrodite Kallipygos was literally the goddess with beautiful buttocks. She was said to have a behind more aesthetically pleasing than any other part of her anatomy. It was so revered that a temple was built in its honour, thereby making the buttocks the only part of the human body so honoured.

The human buttocks have provoked both mirth and desire throughout history. They have been called many names; the arse (11th century), the bum (15th century), the backside (16th century), the behind, the bottom and the derriere (18th century), the sit-upon and the tush, (19th century), the buns, the fanny and the keester (20th century).

In *Lady Chatterley's Lover* D. H. Lawrence says "slumberous, round stillness of the buttocks", and Rimbaud admires them as "Two outstanding arcs", while Byron admitted that the female behind is "A strange and beautiful thing to behold." More recent authors have remarked, "That the ass is the face of the soul of sex" and that it offers "a buffet of delights". Italian film director Federico Fellini commented, equally obscurely "the arsy woman is a molecular epic of femininity". Spanish artist Salvador Dali went even further, insisting that "it is through the arse that life's greatest mysteries can be fathomed".

Many fertility carvings depict women with large buttocks; it is likely that our primeval ancestors mated from behind, like the primates, so the pre-human sexual signal of the female came from the rear as with other species. The sexiest females were the ones with large buttocks. Certainly the female bottom is very important in many cultures in the world and large bottoms 'steatopygia' typify fertility and a sexually receptive female. Even in Victorian times, the rear end was emphasized by the invention of the bustle; with hoops and padding to extend the back of ladies shirts. Although I am sure that Victorian ladies would have been horrified by this sexual implication. Today's fashions emphasise the bottom with tight trousers, often low waist bands and glimpses of underwear and bottom crack even fashionable.

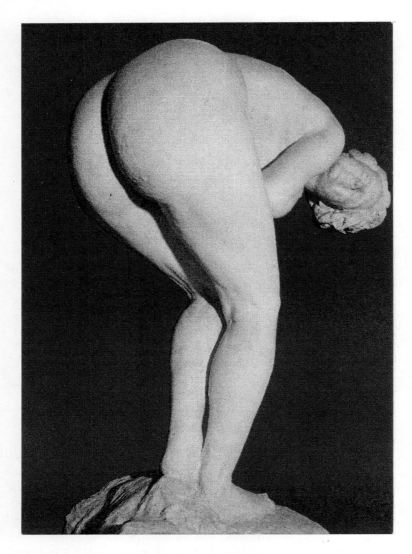

La Giumenta from the Musco Archaeological National in Naples

The word 'booty' became a euphemism, for buttock that originated from the black American music and became slang. Also 'bootylicious', which defined sexually attractiveness with curvaceous buttocks.

The 21st century has become the time of the bottom with artists like Jennifer Lopez. In Brazil they even invented a new word to describe a woman with a large, beautiful bum. 'Popozuda' and the Brazilian music scene saw a growing cult of Popozuda Rock 'n' Roll.

Because of their sexual implication, interpersonal buttock contracts are also somewhat restricted. Outside the sphere of loving couples; a slap on the behind can only be used safely as a signal of friendship between friends; else the action could be misconstrued as inappropriate if not 'politically correct'.

Between lovers, buttock clasping is common in both courtship and in copulation; it is a frequent accompaniment of advanced stages of petting and lovemaking. It has long been the custom in Italy for men to pinch an attractive woman on the behind. The author of the book *How to be an Italian* listed three fundamental pinches:

• The Pizzicato, a quick tweaking pinch performed with the thumb and middle finger. Recommended for beginners.

• The Vivace a more vigorous, multi fingered pinch performed several times in quick succession.

• The Sustenuto a prolonged, rather heavy handed rotating pinch for the use on 'living girdles'.

I would like to see any amorous Italian try this in the UK. They would more that likely end up with a black eye.

Women too can appreciate a pert male bottom and there have been many trends and fashions throughout history that have brought attention to this part of the male anatomy, not least the tight jeans of the 20th century.

The Anus

The female anus

According to estimates, about 50 percent of Western women have experimented with anal intercourse at some time in their lives. Only a small percentage finds it pleasurable, but in many parts of the world anal sex is a normal part of their lovemaking.

Anatomically, the anus is loaded in nerve endings, so that it has the potential to be a source of physical pleasure. However, its role is an exit rather than an entrance, meaning that sex it not a natural function of this orifice. The anus should be very well lubricated before being penetrated; you should never transfer the penis from the anus to the vagina; the bacteria in the anus would cause problems to the vaginal membranes.

Other cultures have often used the female anus for sexual gratification there may have been cultural reasons for this:

• In early centuries, before condoms were accessible, anal sex was used as a primitive form of birth control. This is explicitly shown in Pre-Columbian pottery figurines from ancient Peru. Whenever a couple are shown together, having sex, vaginal penetration is shown unless there is a baby sleeping next to them. When there is a baby present the artist clearly shows anal penetration. This manner of contraception has survived right up to the present day in many parts of the world, especially in Latin America, parts of Africa and the East. Wherever condoms are not available, for whatever reason, poverty, ignorance or religious dogma, there is the likelihood that, despite the health risks, anal penetration will be employed as a simple form of birth control.

• A second reason is that it allows young couples to engage in sexual encounters before marriage without the female partner losing her virginity. This is particularly true in certain Mediterranean cultures, where the display of a bloodied sheet in the morning following the wedding is demanded as proof of the bride's intact hymen.

• A third reason has to do with the widespread male dislike of menstrual blood. Because the human female remains sexually receptive when she is menstruating, the male will often want to enjoy sex at those times, but is inhibited from doing so because of bleeding; anal sex provides them with an alternative entrance at this time.

The Male Anus

In this book I have not made much mention of homosexual sex but of course the male bottom and anus are the main erotic areas of titillation and anal sex in common between homosexual couples. The same rules apply the anus not being a natural entrance it should be well lubricated before entry.

Chapter 6

Homeopathy

The love of two pure lovers consists of desire and in mutual pleasing
In it nothing can be worthwhile unless their will be equal.

Jaufre Rudel

omeopathy can help in any programme to boost a low sex drive. Homeopathic medicine is based on the belief that natural substances can stimulate the body's own healing powers to relieve the symptoms and signs of sickness. Natural substances are selected which, if used at full strength, would produce symptoms in a healthy person similar to those it is designed to treat. For example, substances are used that, given full strength, would lower libido. In homeopathic doses however, the opposite effect occurs and sex drive increases. This is the first principle of homeopathy that 'like cures like'.

The second main principle of homeopathy is that increasing dilution of a solution has the opposite effect of increasing its potency, that 'less cures more'. By diluting noxious and even poisonous substances many millions of times, their healing properties are enhanced while their undesirable side effects are lost.

Homeopathic remedies should ideally be taken on their own, without eating or drinking for at least 30 minutes before or after. Tablets should also be taken without handling; tip them into the lid of the container, or into a teaspoon to transfer them to your mouth, then suck or chew them. Do not swallow them whole, always dissolve them in the mouth.

Homeopathy should not be linked with Aromatherapy or other complementary therapies unless specified by a trained therapist. Sometimes symptoms get worse before they get better, especially if you are using homeopathy alone. This is known as aggravation. Try to persevere as it is a good sign that the remedy is working. When taking homeopathic remedies avoid drinking tea or coffee as these may interfere with the homeopathic effect. It is best to see a trained homeopath that can assess your constitutional type, personality, lifestyle, family background, likes and dislikes as well as our symptoms before deciding which treatment is right for you.

Homeopathic Hormones

Homeopathic hormones may be used to improve sex drive; levels of the following hormones may be measured, in saliva, and may also be plotted over time to see how they are changing in, for example, women whose low sex drive is linked with menstrual problems or menopausal symptoms:

- Oestrogen
- Oestradiol
- Progesterone
- Testosterone
- Cortisol
- DHEA
- Thyroxine

Often an imbalance is found between cortisol and DHEA levels when low sex drive is due to stress. Low sex drive is also often linked with comparatively low levels of testosterone in both men and women. Homeopathic DHEA and homeopathic testosterone therefore form two important cornerstones in the homeopathic treatment of low libido. The following remedies can be taken, start with 6c potency two of three times a day for up to a week. If relief occurs but the symptoms return once you stop taking the remedy, you can increase the effect by taking 30c potency.

Homeopathic Remedies for Low Sex Drive

Agnus castus (chaste tree)
Best used in cases where you have lost interest in sex and/or have low sex drive that could be due to menopause in women or anxiety and depression leading to premature ejaculation in men.

Amphosca
Amphosca is best used by both partners where they have lost interest in sex with each other. There is a men's version and a woman's version with slightly different constituents. The women's version contains an ovarian extract, ovarinum, and the men's contains a testicular extract, orchitinum.

Arsenicum album (arsen alb: arsenic oxide)
Arsen alb is useful where low sex drive is linked with anxiety and fear of failure, restlessness, tiredness and nervousness.

Baryta carbonica (baryta carb: barium carbonate)
Baryta carb is helpful for men with low sex drive and little interest in sex. It can help impotence when linked with low sex drive. It will help men with low confidence and anxiety about their body or size of their penis.

Bach Rescue remedy
Rescue remedy is a homeopathic preparation designed to help people cope with life's traumas. It will help in any situation of stress and nervousness. The remedy contains five flower essences: Cherry Plum, Clematis, Impatiens, Rock Rose and Star of Bethlehem preserved in grape alcohol (brandy).

Cactus grandiflorus (cactus grand: night flowering cactus)
This is useful for women whose low sex drive and aversion to sex results in painful spasm of the vaginal muscles when ever penetration is attempted (vaginismus).

Calcarea carbonica (calc carb: calcium carbonate)
Calc carb is useful where low sex drive is linked with physical exhaustion and anxiety, weight gain and profuse sweating linked to menstrual problems or menopause.

Cimicifuga (cimic: black cohosh)
Cimicifuga is useful for women with low sex drive linked with gynaecological problems; menstruation, menopause, pregnancy, postnatal depression and other hormonal imbalances.

Conium maculatum (hemlock)
Conium is helpful for men who have low sex drive linked with anxiety, erectile flaccidity or prostrate problems.

Cuprum metallicum (cuprum met: elemental copper)
Cuprum metallicum is useful for treating low sex drive that is linked with exhaustion and mental fatigue or for those who have suffered from sexual suppression.

Ferrum picricum (iron picrate)
Ferrum picricum helps men with low sex drive linked to prostate or urinary problems, pain in the urethra and urinary retention.

Folliculinum (ovarian follicle extracts)
Foliculinum is made from ovarian follicle extracts and is helpful for women whose low sex drive is linked with fluid retention, cyclical breast pain and mood swings.

Gelsemium sempervirens (gelsemium: yellow jasmine)
Gelsemium is useful where low sex drive is associated with exhaustion, heavy limbs, generalized lack of energy, headaches or dizziness and fear of sex.

Graphites (graphite: pencil lead)
Graphites are prescribed for men who do not like sex, may have premature ejaculation or have a problem getting an erection. For women it is helpful for low libido associated with dislike or fear of sex, especially when accompanied by vaginal dryness and difficult entry.

Kali carbonicum, (kali carb: potassium carbonate)
Kali carb is useful for women whose loss of sex drive is linked with tiredness and tension after intercourse, also those who fear letting go and cannot relax.

Lachesis (bushmaster snake venom)
Lachesis is helpful where low sex dive is linked with depression that grows as the day goes on. It is also useful for women with hormonal problems connected to irregular periods, menopause and hot flushes.

Love life
Love life Homeopathic Tincture is a complex remedy for low sex drive containing a number of homeopathic ingredients, including Agnus castus, American arum, Baryta Carb, Cinchone, Sepia and Selenium Phoshorica. It is complemented by love life tablets containing a variety of oriental herbs, vitamins and minerals.

Lycopodium clavatum (lycopodium: club moss)
For men lycopodium is helpful where low sex drive is linked with impotence as one get older, prostrate problems and tiredness in the later part of the day, it can also help with erectile dysfunction. For women it is good for low sex drive linked with vaginal dryness and discomfort during intercourse.

Moschus moschiferus (moschus: musk deer)
Moschus is made from the sexual secretions of the musk deer that are designed to attract females. It helps with low sex drive, linked to exhaustion and anxiety.

Natrum muriaticum (natrum mur: rock salt)
Natrum muriaticum helps with low sex drive linked with worry, depression and strong emotion. In women it helps where there is an aversion to sex; perhaps due to vaginal discomfort and dryness or a bad sexual experience.

Nux vomica (nux vom: poison nut)
Nux vomica is useful for workaholics, the impatient and lack of sex drive due to over activity, insomnia and overindulgence; drugs, alcohol, caffeine or cigarettes.

Phosphoricum acidum (phos. Ac: phosphoric acid)
Phos ac is one of the most effective homeopathic remedies for low sex drive connected to lethargy, sluggishness and stress, also for those with guilt feelings about sex. It helps those who have been told that there is shame in masturbation, wet dreams and enjoying sex just for itself.

Platinum metallicum (elemental platinum)
Platinum is helpful for women with low sex drive linked to gynaecological problems and difficulty in achieving intercourse because of fear and pain.

Plumbum metallicum (Plumbum met: elemental lead)
For men Plumbum met is useful for low sex drive linked with heart conditions and hardening of the arteries, leading to erectile dysfunction. For women Plumbum met helps with aversion to sex resulting from painful spasm of the vaginal muscles.

Populace tremuloides (American aspen)
Populace tremuloides is helpful for men whose low sex drive is linked with prostrate problems and difficulty urinating.

Pulsatilla nigricans (pulsatilla: pasque flower)
Pulsatilla is very helpful for low sex drive associated with tiredness, weepiness and women with menstrual or menopausal problems.

Rhus toxicodendron (rhus tox: poison ivy)
Rhus tox is useful for low sex drive linked to severe depression that comes at night leading to weeping and insomnia; often caused by loneliness.

Sepia (sepia: cuttlefish ink)
Sepia is prescribed for women with severe aversion to sex, linked with exhaustion, and indifference to sexual partners, and a tendency to feel lonely, tearful and claustrophobic in a relationship. It has been found very helpful for women who do not like to be touched, and have bad body image due to overweight and/or food cravings. Sepia can help with menopause to relieve hot flushes and night sweats and can be taken every hour as necessary.

Staphysagria (larkspur)
Staphysagria is helpful for women whose low sex drive and sexual aversion is linked with their health, hysterectomy, or unresolved anger and resentment.

Sulphur (flowers of sulphur)
For men sulphur is useful when low sex drive is linked with pain in the penis, scrotum and erectile dysfunction. For women it is used with premenstrual syndrome, insomnia, lack of energy and menopause.

Many of these remedies are now available over the counter, but it is always preferable to seek the help of a fully qualified homeopathic therapist before taking any homeopathic remedy and let your doctor know when you are taking any other prescribed medicine.

Chapter 7

Mayday, and the Sexual Rites of Spring

May Day or Beltane is one of the four Grand Sabbaths, the others being Halloween (Samhain, the ushering in of winter,) Christmas (winter solstice) and Mid Summer's Eve (summer solstice.) Beltane is celebrated between sundown on 30th April and sundown on 1st May, to mark the return of spring and the end of winter. It coincides with the obscure Christian festival of Walpurgisnacht, when witches are alleged to meet on the Brocken Mountain in Germany and hold revels with the devil, and was also called Rood Day and Rudemas.

The festival stems from an ancient Celtic Druidic fire celebration and is also regarded as a fertility fire festival. Beltane, or Beltain, is also named after the Irish beltaine meaning 'Bel-fire', the fire of the Celtic God of light. Known as Bel, Beli or Belinus who was a Scottish sun deity. This is the 'Dawning time' the second most significant festival in the witches' year, the most important being another fire festival of the Celts, Hallowe'en.

Beltane was regarded as a fertility rite to ensure the fruitfulness of animals and crops during the coming season. The occasion has long been associated with 'Maypole Dancing' and the 'May Queen'. The decorated maypole offering phallic imagery and tracing back to the decorated Sacred Tree of Mesopotamian religions. The Maypole, which symbolized the ancient cosmic tree and the phallus of the Sky Father, formed the focus of fertility dances.

Morris dancing dates from the 16th century but its origins go back much further and are to do with fertility and the rites of agrarian society. The dancers wear bells at their knees and often wave hankies to attract and welcome benevolent spring and summer spirits, or clash sticks (symbolizing the eternal battle between winter and summer.

The maypole would be hawthorn or birch but in some areas pine is used. In any case the pole must be topped with greenery, which makes it resemble a great phallic symbol, and should be carried by a party of revellers to the spot where it will be raised. It is then festooned with flowers and herbs, and ribbons, red (for the god), white (for the goddess), and green (for nature and fertility), blue and yellow, all colours representing the union of earth and sky, winter and summer, water and fire. These were then entwined and woven into intricate patterns as the dancers circle the pole accompanied by drums and singing and the crowning of the May Queen.

In Wicca, Beltane is the rite to celebrate the sexual union or marriage of the Goddess and the God. According to some, the Horned God, Cernunnos, accepts his paternal and marital responsibilities in respect of the Goddess (who is now bearing his offspring.) He begins the shift, which is completed at midsummer, from the irresponsible hunter of the greenwood to become faithful mate and provider. It celebrates the coming of summer and the flowering of life. The Goddess manifests as the May Queen, Goddess of Flowers, symbol of full summer fertility and love, whose festival was celebrated in Ancient Rome in early May, the final appearance of the Maiden aspect of the Goddess and the time of her marriage to Jack O'Green who is associated with the Horned God.

Even the 'phrygian sibyl' of Roman mythology was an ancestress of the spring goddess, her particular festival being 'hilaria', which was a romp of sensuality. May is thus associated with love of the flirtatious, extra marital kind. This is not the divine marriage, but the moment of the senses overflowing with ripeness. Thus, to go 'A-Maying' was a euphemism for gathering may flowers from the hawthorn and tasting the pleasures of illicit love. Flowers were often beribboned and young suitors would hang their bunch at the door of the girl they liked.

There are many traditional spells connected to Beltane, one uses sage: Pick twelve sage leaves (or use 132 pinches of the dried herb) at midnight on St. Mark's Eve (April 24th, Beltane, Celtic May Eve festival), put four leaves beneath your pillow, burn four as incense and eat the other four. Your dreams will reveal much about your future lovers.

In very early times, if there had been a bad harvest the previous year, the sacrifice of a willing male virgin was made to the fire. By Druidic times the huge wicker man they burned was probably filled with animals. But by the early Christian era a mock male sacrifice was burned, chosen by selecting a piece of carlin cake that was marked with a charred cross from a bag of similar pieces; this is the origin of the hot cross bun.

Sundown on May Eve was the signal for Druids to kindle the great Belfires from nine different kinds of wood by turning an oaken spindle in an oaken socket on top of the nearest beacon hill. By mediaeval times, every village had Beltane fires, which were attributed with both fertility and healing powers; in remote areas of lands where the Celts have settled, they are still lit.

Young couples, at times naked, leapt over the twin Beltane fires, ran between them or danced clockwise. Livestock, after the long winter, were freed from the barns and stables to be driven between two ritual fires so as to cleanse them of disease and ensure their fruitfulness and plentiful milk yield for the approaching year.

But the chief feature of the festival was the custom, that dates back to the first farming communities and finds echoes worldwide, of young couples going into the woods and fields to make love and bring back the first may or hawthorn blossoms to decorate homes and barns. May Day is the only time of the year, according to tradition, that hawthorn may be brought indoors, despite the legend that bringing it in to the house risked fairies coming in too. Make a wish on the dew-bedecked flowers and it will be answered.

Beltane is therefore a potent festival for fertility magic of all kinds, whether it is conceiving a child, the blooming of a financial or business venture or a recovery in health, as we move into light and the warmth of summer weather.

The incense and herbs used at Beltane include almond, angelica, ash, cowslip, frankincense, hawthorn, lilac, marigold, and roses for love. Candle colours for Beltane rituals would include red and silver for passion and secret dreams.

Couples wanting a baby might have sex on May Eve next to one of the old Earth fertility symbols, such as on the phallus of the Cerne Abbas Giant in Dorset. This magic would also be used for securing the harvest; young couples would make love in the fields on May Eve to encourage the Earth to be fertile.

Witches would use a cauldron (or a mirror) for scrying, especially on old festivals such as May Eve, by using pure water and dropping dark inks or oils on the surface. With direct moonlight, or a candle behind you, images will be seen that will suggest ideas or answers to questions or matters that are concerning you.

May dew has often been used for healing and countryside spells. It is said to soothe and heal sore eyes, skin diseases, gout and vertigo and to bring succour for children with fragile health. The dew should ideally be collected from fennel leaves on the dawn of May Day, put on to the eyes it is said to improve the eyesight.

We do not know the origin of when the ancient tradition began of maidens bathing their faces in the May Morning dew; it is preferable to gather it from beneath an oak tree the Druidic tree of wisdom, to enhance their beauty.

May dew was also said to be endowed with the power to enhance fertility and to offer protection against malevolence from others. It would promise luck throughout the year to all who rolled or washed in it, nakedness optional, especially as the Sun rose. Certainly the Druids regarded dew as a powerful fertility symbol as did the many cultures that have celebrated May Day all the way through the years even into the 21st century.

Thus there is much more to May Day than the modern day workers' marches and nature festivals, it is a powerful ancient celebration, so wake up and be joyful for spring has come and is full of potent sexual promise.

Chapter 8

Lips and a History of the Kiss

Of all the ten thousand things created by heaven, man is the most precious.
Off all the things that make man prosper, none can be compared to sexual intercourse.

Li Tung Hsuan. *The Art of the Bedchamber.* (Ars Amatoria)

t is not often considered but human lips are outside the body as opposed to most other mammals where their lips are tucked inside. The lips are one of the most expressive features of our face; we can smile, frown and display many other emotions by the tilt of our lips. Woman have always reddened their lips through-out history but in 17th century Britain the wearing of red lipstick was prohibited because it was "the badge of a harlot and would kindle a fire of lust in the hearts of men unfortunate enough to set eyes on them". Despite repeated suppressions by church and state, lip cosmetics refused to disappear and throughout history kept on bouncing back in fashionable style one way or another. In a lady's magazine of the late 1820's it is clear that a special lip shape had been adopted - the 'cupid bow.'

Some tribes, the Surma in Ethiopia, the Lobi of Ghana and the Sara-Kaba and Ubangi of the Congo in Africa enlarge their lips with plates. Tlingit Indian women in British Columbia displayed large lip-discs and the women with the largest discs enjoyed the highest status. The

Shilluks of Sudan preferred blue-stained lips on their women and the Ainu of Japan like their females to have tattooed lips. In the Philippines a chewing gum made of betel nut is used to redden the lips.

Today the fashion is for the 'bee sting lips' and these are achieved by syringe injections of either collagen or hylaform gel. For permanent reshaping, fat can be taken from the client's bottom and injected into their lips and recent trends in the West are for lip decorations and piercing to bring even more attention to the lips.

The lips are very important in giving visual signals; in a recent survey of the ten most important contact points on a woman's body, the number one female erogenous zone was named as the lips. But in many cultures kissing is taboo; this has been because mouth to mouth kissing has been considered unhygienic. Until recently in countries like Spain and Japan there was a ban on kissing in public.

Kissing is an intimate thing which is why many prostitutes say "no kissing" because kissing is reserved for more personal relationships. Kissing has acted throughout history as a symbol of betrayal and deceit, a symbol of true love and as a tool of seduction. To most lovers the kiss has carried a meaning of a pathway to further sexual relations.

Russians may have been first to bring the kiss into the marriage ceremony by way of sealing the contract, but this is universally accepted as part of the marriage ceremony. There are twenty different words in French and thirty in German for the word 'kiss'.

Erotic mouth kissing has an intriguing origin. When lovers bring their open lips together and start probing the interior of one another's mouths with their tongues, the so-called 'deep kiss, French kiss or soul kiss', they are performing an action that harks back to primitive times. Before convenient 'baby food' was available prehistoric tribal women used to wean their infants off breast milk and on to solid foods by pre-chewing the food in their own mouths until it was soft and semi-liquid. Thus mouth probing became a caring act and kissing a sign of love and nurture. From this ancient beginning grew the deep kissing of loving adults. We no longer need to do this but it can still are seen that mothers will bite off a piece of food to give to a child and in some love play food is transferred from one partner's mouth to another.

Modern physiologists will link kissing with the mother/child relationship, but Freud had a very negative attitude towards adults who enjoy kissing, perhaps because his own mouth caused him endless agony. He suffered from cancer of the palate, and had 33 operations on his mouth.

As far back as 1500BC the first erotic kiss was exchanged in India, according to anthropologist Vaughn Bryant Jr. He says there is no recorded evidence in wall paintings or art of kissing before then. More recently in Asia it was not considered hygienic to kiss on the lips and in Indian cinema it has only just recently become a feature of Bollywood films. And even then the two actors involved may well be asked to have a medical to make sure that they could not pass on anything unhealthy in this way.

From 1353BC to 1336BC kissing was depicted in Egyptian art during the time of the pharaoh Akhenaten. Scholars believed that Egyptians equated the act with giving life. From 753BC to AD476 the kiss signified respect and submission to the Romans. Roman men are said to have kissed their wives when they arrived home from battle to judge if they had been dipping into the wine cellar during their absence.

In the 1st century AD the gesture took a role in the Christian communion rite as a 'kiss of peace'. But in the reformation of the 16th century, the kiss of peace became associated with the kiss by which Judas Iscariot betrayed Jesus according to the bible and it faded from the Christian ritual.

In the 6th century kissing became part of the French courtship ritual. And from the 9th to the 12th century court troubadours played out their acts of love and chivalry by kissing the lady's hand or the hand of their lord and this was part of the oath to honour and defend. From the 9th century under the feudal system a vassal knelt before his overlord putting his hands in those of his lord's and declaring himself his man. The overlord then bound himself by kissing the vassal raising him to his feet.

In 1744 the 'Kiss of life' method of resuscitation was first described in an account by the Scottish physician William Tossach. It only became established medical practise in the 1950's, held back by notions of impropriety. In the early 1800s Admiral Nelson was said to have asked his flag Captain to "Kiss me, Hardy" (some say Kismet Hardy) on his deathbed. Literature and letters from the trenches of World War One describe dying soldiers exchanging kisses in acts of intimacy that was said to unite souls. John C Rice and May Irwin were the first actors filmed kissing in Thomas Edison's 18 second piece, '*The Kiss*', also known as '*the Widow Jones*'. The longest screen kiss was exchanged between Regis Toomey and Jane Wyman in the 1941 feature film '*You're in the army now*' and lasted over three minutes. This record may have been broken by now.

Ancient scrolls were found in Nag Hammadi in Egypt in 1945 that revealed an early history of Christianity. One line, with gaps where holes existed in the scroll said about Jesus; "that his … companion Mary Magdalene was loved more that all his disciples and that he used to kiss her often on the..." this indicates that Jesus and Mary were lovers. In religious ceremony the kiss of peace or Pax was used until it was rejected by the Protestants in Germany. The Catholic religion still uses the kiss in respect to the kissing of the ring or foot of the Pope.

The 'kiss of shame' was the name of the kiss given in Satanist ritual, this kiss is the one used to pledge oneself to the devil. The kiss would be given to the high priest or priestess or to an animal usually a goat, which would represent Satan. The kiss would often be placed on the posterior, anus or private parts of the subject. The 19th century theologian Johann Joseph von Glorres regarded this kiss as a sign of the heretic's promise of eternal servitude to the Devil, suggesting the perversion of normal Christian rituals. The witches Sabbath was an inverted Eucharist, hence the modern term 'black mass'. It was also believed that the devil's face was impressed on the bottom of these creatures and the witch or priest was actually kissing the lips of the devil when they kissed the posterior.

So how does this explain the phrase 'kiss my arse'? To understand this it is necessary to examine early engravings that depicts the devil. The devil does not have buttocks according to mythology, where his buttocks should be, he has another face. This second face is the one that was supposed to be kissed by witches as part of the ritual of the Sabbath. Accused of the filthy action of kissing the Devil's rump, they reputedly defended themselves by insisting that they had only kissed the mouth of this second face. The kiss of shame was therefore transformed into the symbol of devil brotherhood or witches' sisterhood.

The 'sinister kiss' was when a vampire would bite and draw blood, an adaptation of this is the love bite where, mostly younger people or adolescents, would bite and leave a mark on each other's necks.

In the late 18th century kissing between men became less acceptable because of the increase in homophobia. Today it is common to see men kiss in public, footballers are seen to kiss when one scores a goal and actors and actresses are seen exchanging the 'luvie kiss' or 'air kiss' where one kisses the air in front of someone's lips or cheeks.

Children's games have often contained kissing - 'kiss chase' was common in the playgrounds in the 20th century.

Today's tabloids use the 'kiss and tell' sensation where a person sells their story of having an affair with a famous person or celebrity.

Kisses were exchanged for votes in the 1780's and politicians still kiss babies today when out electioneering. Fairgrounds and country fairs also used to have kisses for sale booths often to raise money for charity. Thus our lips have been very important in history from showing facial expression and as a sexual statement throughout all cultures and kissing has had many meanings. In each epoch it has been banned and reviled but had also been rejoiced, so pucker up and kiss your troubles away.

Chapter 9

Ginseng, Root of Man or Root of Heaven?

The earliest ginseng, Panax Ginseng, came from the mountain forests of Manchuria but because ginseng has been in demand for centuries or even millennia, a method was developed for cultivating the plant. As a result, ginseng is now found throughout Eastern Asia and is now grown in many other parts of the world commercially.

Ginseng forms a tap root that may have several heads and it resembles the mandrake root (*Mandragora officinarrum*). The root can grow as long as 50 cm but is usually harvested while much smaller. It has firm white flesh that, when dried, becomes as hard as a rock and can be stored for long periods. The plant has a single stalk, from which emerge dark green five fingered branched leaves. The end of the stalk, which can be 60 cm long, is crowded by a hermaphrodite white umbel (flower-like cluster). Ginseng is the most renowned and sought after health panacea and aphrodisiac in Asia. The root contains a mixture of active substances that strengthen the body, the effect of ginseng only becomes manifest when it is used regularly.

In traditional Chinese medicine 'health' is the key word. In the rule of the yellow Emperor, (third century BCE), was published the first great work on the ancient Chinese system of medicine, this principle is clearly expressed:

"A wise physician never treats an ailment; he prevents the ailment. A wise statesman never brings peace to his country; he maintains peace

in his country. When the physician waits until an ailment has developed, or the statesman waits until troubles arise, then it is too late to heal the one or prevent the other. You would not wait until you are thirsty to dig a well or wait until war has begun to start making weapons."

The Taoist theory of Yin and Yang was also applied to medical thinking. Yin and yang are the two cosmic energies that complement one another and comprise the poles of a unity. The entire universe is an expression of the continuous interplay between these two energies. Taoist philosophy divides the ten thousand beings according to these two principles. Yin is associated with the feminine, the dark, the moon, the earth, while yang is associated with the masculine, the light, the sun, the heavens. The universe is intact only as long as yin and yang, earth and heaven, are joined together in harmony. And a person is healthy only as long as yin and yang are in harmony according to these medical rules.

Some types of disease break out when someone has been exposed to the cold, the wind, the rain or the heat for too long; when there is an inequality between yin and yang; or through the greatest joy or the deepest sorrow; by eating irregularly; self inflicted abuse from drugs; smoking or drinking alcohol; or as a result of unwelcome life situations; or through fear, terror, guilt and bereavement.

The goal of Chinese medicine is to preserve the harmony between yin and yang in a person. For this reason, it is preferred to use preventive and harmonizing medicines. The best of these preventive medicines are ginseng preparations for ginseng maintains the harmony of yin and yang in balance. Ginseng can offer both yin and yang energy. In Chinese medicine a person does not take medicine only after they have become sick; they must take it to remain healthy.

Similarly impotency, procreative weakness, frigidity and premature ejaculation are seen not just as symptoms of, but as expressions of, disturbances in the relationship between yin and yang. Because it is not easy to treat sexual ailments, the Chinese exert themselves to maintain their sexuality in a healthy state. Significantly they have two names for agents they use for such purpose. aphrodisiacs and medicines for yin and yang. They are ingested as preventives and with as few interruptions as possible, a person does not require an aphrodisiac when it is already too late, but utilizes it in order to keep a healthy and gratifying sexual life fresh, pleasurable and active. The aim is to avoid any lessening or atrophy of the sexual experience from the very start. This is the primary reason why ginseng is consumed.

Ginseng is the best known harmonizing medicine of Asia and one of the oldest remedies in the world. We can no longer say when it was first utilized. This wondrous plant whose name means 'man root', is mentioned in the ancient texts. Usually, these speak of a medicinal ginseng wine. Wine was probably the first Chinese medicine, and is referred to as early as the archaic oracle bone inscriptions.

The earliest ginseng roots were found only in the remote mountain areas of Korea; because of their rarity, they were immensely valuable. The value increased if the root had a human appearance. The most valuable roots, which were reserved for the emperor, looked like a man with an erect penis.

Many legends and tales rose up concerning the birth of the coveted root. It was said that a spirit with human form lived in the root, and that she erotically married the ginseng hunter. Rituals intended to mollify the spirits and not disturb the harmony in the forest were developed for digging up the root. The root has always had a strong influence on political decisions in the area and been used as a currency in diplomacy when given as a gift to high officials etc. It was said that ginseng was the 'root of heaven', the plant was almost ritually venerated and was designated foremost of all the tens of thousands of herbs used throughout East Asia. Early legends even suggested that consuming the root could lead to eternal life.

From its beginning, Chinese herbal medicine has been a medicine of experience. In the book of the Prince of Huaina, the legendary first herbalist, we find the following account:

"Sheng Nong tested the taste of hundreds of herbs and drank the water of many springs and fountains, so that humans may know which is sweet and which is bitter. On some days, Sheng Nong tried more that seventy types of poisonous herbs."

The oldest book on herbs, attributed to Sheng Nong himself, includes a passage on the man root:

"Ginseng strengthens the five organs (heart, spleen, lungs, kidney, and liver), soothes the life spirits, harmonizes the soul, removes fears, dispels the forces of evil, makes the eyes radiant, opens the heart, clears out thoughts, and when it is taken for an extended period, fortifies the body for sexual congress and thus prolongs life."

Extraordinarily, this view has not changed during the last millennia. In all of the countries that have been influenced by China, a very large amount of ginseng is consumed every day. It has been long since the supplies of wild root could meet this enormous need. Thus it is now grown commercially all over the world and is affordable for everyone. The wild roots from Korea, however, still fetch astronomical prices when they have an anthropomorphic and phallic form. For it is said that only these are true aphrodisiacs with preventive effect. In China it is believed that a father should give his son such a valuable root only once in his life, usually he is presented with one when he marries.

In the course of history, Chinese, Japanese, and Korean herbalists have developed and tested thousands of mixtures with ginseng and other ingredients. The fresh root can be chewed or swallowed. Dried roots are usually sweetened with sugar. They are also brewed into teas, however a decoction, is more productive. Ginseng is frequently added to an alcoholic beverage. Rice schnapps, bamboo schnapps, brandy, whisky and wine, rice wine or a wine from grapes, are all suitable for this purpose. The root should remain in the liquid for at least three months before it is imbibed. The kaoliang is the best; ginseng roots are extracted in this for three years.

In order to increase the aphrodisiac effects of ginseng, the root is often combined with deer antlers, deer phalli, tiger bones, dried gecko, toad

105

venom, frog concentrate, snake meat, cybister beetles, clasher beetle powder and dragon bones. To increase its use, for a healthy pancreas and to make good aphrodisiacs, ginseng is also mixed with other plants, especially liquorice, ling-chih, ginger, aconite, and rehmannia. As with all ginseng preparations, however, it is important to note that the desired effects only appear when it is taken regularly. There is also a variety of ginseng indigenous to North America (*Panax quinquefolium*) that differs little from its Asian cousins. The North American Indians also referred to this plant as 'man root,' and used it in many ways as a remedy and a love medicine. In North America, however, the ginseng root never attained the same great cultural and medicinal importance as in Eastern Asia.

The Jesuits introduced ginseng to Europe. But the anthropomorphic root was so like the devilish mandrake (Mandragora officinarrum) that it was banned as a tool of witches, while the various systems of Asian medicine were similarly repudiated as devices or the devil. In spite of the Enlightenment, the ginseng root could never gain a foothold in Europe. Instead, it usually met with derision and was largely forgotten.

It was only after numerous laboratory tests were able to demonstrate that ginseng root does indeed contain a mixture of ingredients that improve performance, have general tonic powers and invigorate sexuality that the general interest grew once more. Today ginseng preparations are sold in almost every pharmacy in Europe and North America and powdered ginseng teas and capsules can be purchased around the world.

Some time later Siberian ginseng (*Eleutherocacus senticosus*) attracted worldwide attention. While Siberian ginseng does not belong to the genus Panax, it nevertheless belongs to the same botanical family as genuine ginseng. This shrubby plant is a common sight in the vast sub-arctic plains. For this reason it is also known as taiga root. Strangely Siberian ginseng never found use in the traditional medicine of the area. Its medicinal qualities were not discovered until intensive academic research into ginseng was conducted in the late fifties and early sixties. During this time the soviet physician Gorovoy observed that game animals consumed the shrub with an abandon. As a result, Brekhmann studied the plant thoroughly and conducted a number of experiments with it.

Siberian ginseng has essentially the same stimulating and tonic properties as Panax, but is considerably more effective in laboratory tests. Studies in China have found it helps to prevent altitude sickness; Siberian ginseng is also a well known tonic herb, one that improves general health when taken long term.

Many people have reported improvements in all aspect of their sexual lives. The root fortifies, kindles desire, stabilises the mood and mitigates stress. Can it be that Siberian ginseng is another 'root of heaven'?

Ginseng can have magical uses if the root is carried it will attract love as well as guard one's health, attract money and ensure sexual potency. Ginseng will also bring beauty to all who carry it. Burn ginseng to ward off evil spirits and to break hexes and curses. A tea of ginseng is used as a powerful lust-inducing drink whether alone or mixed with other herbs in teas, wine or other alcoholic beverages.

Hold a ginseng root in your hands, visualize your wish into the root and throw it into running water. Or carve your wish onto a root and toss into the water preferably a running river. Ginseng can be used as a substitute for the more dangerous mandrake in magic of all kinds; particularly protection spells.

Warning
Do not take ginseng when pregnant or if you have high blood pressure, heart palpitations, insomnia, asthma or high fever. It may interact with caffeine, other stimulants, and anticoagulant drugs. Prolonged use of ginseng can cause stomach irritation.

Chapter 10

Chocolate, Food of the Gods

The Greek name for chocolate means 'food of the gods.' Depending who you believe this seductive substance is, an aphrodisiac, highly addictive and good for the heart; others blame it for spots, obesity and stressed-out nerves. But chocolate is good for you, it has properties that make you feel good, it suppresses the irritated throat that makes you cough and could be used in cough medicines. Some studies say that chemicals called flavones present in cocoa can lower blood pressure, and fight the tendency of blood to clot on long haul flights. Chocolate may also boost production of mood chemicals, like serotonin and dopamine, producing a low intensity short lived but genuine high that can lift the spirits and I have known many students take a piece of chocolate into an exam to help stimulate the brain. Chocolate contains antioxidant compounds, which are also found in tea and red wine, where they have gained a reputation for cutting the risk of heart disease.

Pure chocolate is not fattening but the sugar, milk and vegetable fats that are added to it are calorie laden. And as we tend to eat more generally, when we are depressed, it is easy to blame chocolate for those added pounds.

It is not scientifically true that chocolate gives you spots, it is more likely that you get spots from hormonal changes in the body and you eat more chocolate to cheer you up when depressed or use it is an aid to combat depression.

Chocolate makes you feel good, it is a substitute for love, sending warm romantic and loving feelings to the brain. What almost everyone agrees is that chocolate is one of the most irresistible foodstuffs ever produced. Young and old alike love its bitter sweet, almost indescrib-able taste and now we learn that chocolate has been on the world's menus for a lot longer than was previously thought.

According to a recent report traces of chocolate have been found in pots from Mayan graves in Mexico. Some of the pots dated back to 600BCE, pushing back the earliest chemical evidence of chocolate use by more than a 1,000 years. The remains of 14 jugs were sent to the laboratories of Hershey Foods in the USA, for analysis, and according to *Nature* magazine, they found traces of cocoa in three of them.

Other studies suggested that chocolate has the same effect on the brain as falling in love. So what is the secret of this modest bean, which has escaped from the jungles of South America to enchant the palates of the world?

Chocolate is made from the seeds of the tree *Theobroma Cacao*. Theo is Greek for God and Broma means food, so that chocolate is literally 'God food' or 'divine snack'.

The ancient Aztecs of Mexico and Mayans of Belize worshipped, as well they might, the cacao tree and used chocolate beans as a form of currency. Their god Quetzalcoatl was assigned the role of Chocolate Protector on High. It was Native American Indians hit upon the idea of crushing the beans, boiling them in water, adding spices and drinking the hot, tasty, frothy drink.

When the Spaniards landed in South America in the 16th century Montezuma introduced them to chocolate in Mexico City and they wrote how the natives would shake their chocolate brews until a head of foam was built up. The Indians, it seems, liked their cocoa frothy. Christopher Columbus stole a native boat full of beans in 1502 and sent some to King Ferdinand of Spain as an example of the 'coin' used in the New World.

The first shipment of what the Aztecs call 'xocoatl' to the old world was not made until 1520, by the conqueror of Mexico, Hernan Cortes. He sent three· chests of beans to his emperor Charles V, with a note describing how the drink should be prepared.

The Amerindians believed that chocolate was a delicacy of the gods they brewed it like a sacrament, they added chilies and spices and it was given as a gift to nobles and honoured guests. The natives didn't just drink chocolate, they considered it to be an aphrodisiac, tonic and stamina builder and it was used in rituals to their gods. There is a saying in Spanish 'como agua para chocolate' (like water for chocolate,) that means to be sexy and passionate.

The Mexican molé, bitter chocolate sauce, served with chicken, meat and fish is a direct descendant of the ancient Aztec recipes. Made by the Peruvians Indians from the cacao bean, chocolate was offered to deities at births, weddings, puberty rites and funerals as well as so generals and to the bravest soldiers after battle. It was also the standard currency in Peru.

The indigenous people believed in the power of chocolate as an aphrodisiac, Montezuma, who maintained a harem of 600 odalisques, was said to drink 50 cups of it a day from a goblet of solid gold.

The first foreigners to receive cacao beans disregarded them; in 1502 Christopher Columbus gave some to King Ferdinand of Spain, who was not interested. Sir Frances Drake brought a ton of them back to England, taken from a Spanish galleon together with bars of silver, but the cocao beans were mistaken for sheep droppings and thrown into Plymouth harbour, thus robbing Queen Elizabeth 1 of a fascinating experience.

Eventually chocolate became accepted and Casanova recommended it as an aphrodisiac. Madam Du Barry, Louis XV's mistress gave it to her lovers and the entourage of Louis XIV drank it several times a day.

In 1616 a committee called the Doctors of the Church called chocolate "the damnable agent of necromancers and sorcerers". In 17th century

England the royal physical Henry Stubbs, declared that "chocolate is provocative to lust." Research chemists now admit that it is a mild aphrodisiac. Chocolate contains caffeine and theobromine, both of which stimulate the central nervous system and phenylethylamine, which is similar to amphetamines and has an effect rather like the emotional highs and lows of being in love.

In 1808 Dufour, a French restaurateur' wrote that "chocolate was a cure for digestive disorders and sexual dysfunction."

Alexander Dumas, in his *Grand dictionair de cuisine*, suggests making chocolate the night before and leaving it: "The repose of the night concentrates it, and gives it a velvet quality. Then reheat it and serve in a porcelain coffee pot." He recommends it as an aphrodisiac and as a pick me up after lovemaking.

Chocolate was slow to gain popularity in Europe until people started to add sugar to the brew and it gradually caught on, along with coffee, the other main export from the new world. Chocolate was extremely expensive and high profits were being made. Cocoa plantations were founded all over the colonized world and the tropical empires of the European powers flourished on this trade.

The conversion of chocolate from drink to food began in the 1700s, when cocoa was added to cakes and ice creams. The chocolate bar, as we know it today, still lay far in the future. The first attempts at making solid chocolate came in the early 1800s when cocoa beans were ground into dust, heated then pressed into moulds after being sweetened. The resulting product was delicious, some thing like the chocolate truffles we eat today, but had a short shelf life. Dutch chemist and food scientist Coenrad Van Houten who, in 1825, perfected a process whereby cocoa butter was created, invented proper chocolate bars that we would now recognise. The fatty essence of the cocoa bean was extracted from cocoa beans after subjecting them to very high pressure.

Scientists then found ways of making even smoother and darker chocolate. In the 1880's, Rudolph Lindt of Switzerland started adding extra cocoa to make a pure, glossy product that melts at 36C, just a degree below the core temperature of the human body. This allowed the chocolate to melt in the mouth but not melt on a warm day. Another Swiss, Daniel Peter, added condensed milk to chocolate, making a sweeter and smoother rival to dark chocolate.

Today chocolate aficionados seem to be divided between dark chocolate and milk chocolate and are fiercely loyal to their own taste. Dark chocolate fans would say that milk chocolate is defiled and sugurified and only fit for children.

Chocolate is advertised as sensual; an arouser of the senses and it is often a gift for lovers to exchange or a consolation for the lovelorn.

In recent years there has been a battle between British chocolate makers and those in Europe, this is because in Britain manufacturers use less pure chocolate and more vegetable fats. There has been a sort of compromise in this dispute and British chocolate is now allowed to be sold abroad as 'family chocolate'.

If chocolate is king, cure all, and the food of the gods, then long may it reign, as a feel good food and for its aphrodisiac properties.

Chapter 11

Honey the Sweetest Thing

He who feels that he is weak for coition should drink before going to bed a glassful of very thick honey and eat twenty almonds and one hundred kernels of the pine tree. He must follow the regime for three nights.

Sheikh Nefzawi, *The Perfumed Garden.*

Many an Oriental aphrodisiac dish has honey as a frequent ingredient. Galen a Greek of the 2nd century A.D and court physical to the Emperor Marcus Aurelius also recommended as an effective aphrodisiac, a glass of thick honey, taken before bedtime, together with the consumption of almonds and one hundred grains of the pine tree. The recipe was to be followed for three consecutive nights. A compound of honey, pepper and ginger is also recommended as an aphrodisiac by 13th century Arab physician Avicenna.

Honey contains bee pollen which may account for its reputed pro-sexual effect. Honey was widely used in poultices applied to the lingam (male member) to increase its size in ancient India, and mixed with crocodile dung, olive oil and lemon juice for use as a contraceptive barrier by women. Honey can also be used as a lubricant and a delicious agent in the introduction to the pleasures of oral sex.

An erotic game called 'The tree' in Japan where some lovers prefer to lick honey or/and yogurt from one another's naked bodies; while doing so they might reflect that 'lechery' comes from the word for 'licking.' Honey has often been used in erotic literature to lubricate the sexual organs and add interest to the tongue. In Arabia honey and yogurt were often used on the male or female genitals as a prelude to oral sex.

According to the Roman poet Ovid, author of the *Ars Amatoria*, honey was a great aphrodisiac. Hydromel is a beverage consisting of honey and water, once taken as an aphrodisiac.

The honey bee, *Apis mellifera L*, preceded humans on earth by 10-20 million years. Honey bees are one of the oldest forms of animal life still in existence from the Neolithic Age. Primeval humans gathered and ate the honey and honeycombs of wild bees, the only available sweetening, as far back as 7000 BCE.

Bronze Age societies celebrated triumphs by drinking mead, probably the first intoxicating beverage, fermented from honey. In fact, the words mead and mellifera (the specific name for honey bees), which are similar in several languages, were derived from the root words referring to honey, bees, liquor, doctored drink, etc. In the past, words for mead, honey and honeybee have been used interchangeably, revealing the importance placed on the alcoholic beverage derived from honey.

Like honey, beeswax has been prominent in ancient folklore and mythology. In the pre Christian era, wax was offered as a sacrifice to the gods; featured in the rites of birth, circumcision, marriage, purification and death and was used in embalming, sealing coffins, and mummification. The use of beeswax in religious candles carried over into Christian times and led to beekeeping by clergy and monks in order to ensure an adequate supply of this raw material.

Since ancient times beeswax has been shaped into candles in the shape of people for use in love magic; this custom still continues today in Haiti and in American voodoo cults. The red candle is said to kindle passion and the black would have the opposite effect.

In the past, beeswax served as a medium of exchange and taxation; it was exacted as tribute from conquered nations and was used in writing, painting, sculpturing, and protecting works of art, as well as for illumination.

Galen (131-200 A.D) recommended honey in general as an invigorating, potency promotion and rejuvenating agent. Pliny considered honey, "a medicine of heaven". Honey was also greatly valued in the Arabic (later Islamic) world and in Indian medicine. Always and everywhere, it was used as an aphrodisiac as well, the Indians frequently using it externally; applying or massaging it onto the genitals. A little honey on the clitoris, for example, is said to heighten the pleasures of cunnilingus.

Honey, beeswax and propolis have been used extensively in pharmacopoeia since 2000 BCE. The principal medicinal value of honey arises from its antibacterial properties when used as a wound dressing.

There are many legends about bees, in ancient Greece the first person to keep bees was one of the sons of Apollo, Aristaeus, but for some reason he displeased the gods and as a punishment all his bees died. Aristaeus was mortified and prayed for forgiveness, he was told that to show his remorse he should sacrifice a bull, leave it in the field and return to it after nine days. When Aristaeus returned to the carcass he was astonished to find a swarm of bees nesting inside the body to the bull, his bees had been reborn and returned to him. Because of this miracle, bees were believed to have power over death, and the ancient Greek kings had mounds placed over their tomb in the shapes of bee hives, so that they too would be reborn. Many people were buried in huge pots, pithoi, filled with honey, which both preserved their flesh and gave them the chance of rebirth, as the bees were born from the honey filled chamber in the hive.

Bees were sacred to the Earth Goddess, Demeter, who was called the pure Mother Bee and especially to Aphrodite, whose priestesses were known as Melissa, which means 'Bees' Aphrodite was also called Melissa, the queen been who annually killed her own consort.

116

In Celtic myth bees were messengers between the worlds, and you could whisper messages to them which they could take to the land of the dead.

Perhaps it is in remembrance of these ideas that in folklore the hives should be covered and the bees told whenever there was a death in the family, or else the bees would swarm and fly away.

Inevitably as Christianity took over other aspects of Pagan belief, it has taken over the magical powers of the bees that became known as 'the Little Servants of God'. And Mary took on the powers of the Pagan goddesses being described in mediaeval hymns as 'a nest of honey' and a 'dripping honeycomb'.

Bees were believed to have all sorts of magical information and knowledge. It was said that they could tell if a girl was a chaste virgin - she should be able to walk through a swarm without being stung.

Bees were also associated both with marriage and with the Moon Goddess; the stars were sometime referred to as the bees of the Moon Goddess. It was believed that if the Moon goddess struck a person with madness, she would fill the head with bees, giving them strange thoughts and fancies.

It was said that when Plato was a baby, some bees landed on his lips as he slept in his cradle, an indication that he would become known for his honeyed words. And still today full lips are referred to as 'bee stung'.

When amber was ground up and mixed with honey, it was thought to improve the eyesight, while adding rose-oil to the mixture transferred the site of the cure from the eye to the ear, where it was used to heal infections and, in some cases, cure deafness. In 1623 it was reported that Pope Urban V11 owned a piece of amber containing three bees.

Who put the honey in honeymoon? Among various claims for the word's origins, one of the sweeter theories is that its medieval Saxon roots refer to a month long period when newlyweds would take honey every day to promote fertility and sustain desire and performance. A growing number of people firmly believe that honey, and other products of beehives are as deserving of a place in the bedroom as well as the kitchen. It has been highly prized as an aphrodisiac by many cultures.

It is said that if you put a woman who's struggling to conceive on bee pollen you can pretty much guarantee a result within two to three months. The belief is that pollen increases the biological value of the egg, restores and rejuvenates natural hormonal substances and can increase sexual stamina. Miraculous qualities have always been attributed to honey and its byproducts. Rock paintings from 11,000 BC in the Madhya Pradesh region of India celebrate bee farming and ancient Egypt prized honey as both medicine and delicacy. Even Dame Barbara Cartland was known to extol the praises of royal jelly, a completely pure and wonderful aid to beauty. The queen of romantic novels lived to the ripe old age of 98.

Honey contains sugars in a natural form that is quick and easy to absorb from tongue to bloodstream in seven minutes, and has been proven to improve athletic performance. Many athletes and swimmers eat it as part of their diet. It contains proteins, vitamins, minerals and enzymes, which die at temperatures above 40C/104F, so for full effect honey should not be heated; it also helps our bodies absorb vital elements like calcium. Bee pollen on the other hand is a complete food as well as a relaxant, and according to the National Institute of Medical Herbalists, royal jelly is well known for its anti-viral properties.

Honey bees originated in Southern Asia, probably in the region of Afghanistan. The earliest record of humans gathering honey from the wild colonies is from 7000 BCE. Man first kept bees about 3000 – 4000 BCE perhaps as early as 5000 BCE. There is no way of knowing to what extent honeybees have evolved since then. We can assume that some evolution has taken place, particularly with regard to the social organization of the colony and foraging behaviour. Apis mellifera is the most widely distributed of the species of Apis.

The first record of the introduction of honeybees to the western hemisphere was in 1530, in South America. Colonists introduced it to North America from Holland in 1638. Since bees visit a broad range of host plants and are able to conserve heat by clustering, they have become widely dispersed and are now found throughout the world. Honey bees are limited in their distribution mainly by an absence of suitable forage. Carolus Linnaeus gave the honeybee the scientific name *Apis mellifera*, in 1858, (it literally mean the (honey-carrying bee)

A more descriptive name, '*A mellifica*, or the honey-making bee', was proposed in 1761. While this second name more accurately describes honey bees (which carry nectar but make honey), the governing bodies of the time dictated that the earlier name be retained. Nevertheless, the term *A Mellifica* can still be found in some bee literature.

Honey bees and their life history and products were topics of study for early philosophers, such as Aristotle, Pliny, and Virgil. Many others have studied bees through history yet most basic knowledge of the natural history of the honey bee has been gathered only since the sixteenth century.

According to Greek mythology, the infant Zeus, out of gratitude for the honey that sustained him, gave the honey bee its sting for defence. Because the bee abused this power, Zeus later decreed that the bee must die whenever the sting is used. Perhaps it is ironic that now we have developed the means to milk venom from bees and use this product in medicine. The collection and sale of bee venom is an increasingly popular although extremely limited enterprise. Presently its greatest use is in the treatment of bee venom hypersensitivity. It is also reported as helpful in reducing the pain caused by certain types of arthritis, improving energy levels and heightening the libido.

Wild honey is especially sought after as a remedy and aphrodisiac. The Mexican honey (miel virgin), is produced by wild, sting-less bees, which comes from the Selva Lacandona. Another wild honey, su kung, comes from the provinces of Ti-ch'iang and Kuan Chang. One Chinese book on herbs states that untreated, wild honey has the property of "strengthening the will, making the burdens of the body lighter and banishing hunger and the infirmities of old age".

In addition to honey, other bee products are also used as aphrodisiacs. The Callhuaya Indians of Bolivia collect wild honey; they press the comb and collect the honey that flows from it. The remains are known as pogo. It is ingested as a remedy for infertility and impotence. Mixed with maté (*llex paraguariensis*) and oregano it is brewed into an aphrodisiac tea.

Honey and bee products have been a vital part on the industry and substance of mankind. Indeed some birds actually cooperate with man to find honey and share in the bounty. And many animals including humans rely on honey as a part of their diet. Honey it truly the sweetest thing and bees must be admired for their stamina and devotion within the hive and in bringing this divine substance to the world.

Chapter 12
Bath Time Magic

ince ancient times, bathing has been considered indispensable to emotional and physical health. Hypocrites knew that
good health requires both a healthy body and a healthy
mind. In Hypocrites' *Aphorisms*, he wrote, "Aromatic baths
are useful in the treatment of impotence and of female
disorders."

As far back as 4000 B.C. the ancient Egyptians used bathing as a means
of healing and lifting spirits, and certain aromatic baths were believed
to produce magical and sexual effects on the body and to revive sexual
vigour. They discovered that aromas and perfumes can have a profound
affect on a person's physical, emotional and mental states. The
Egyptians were very fond of bathing and perfumed oils were often used
in their baths to treat both body and psyche.

Kyphi was the opium of the masses, used as a liquid perfume and
known to produce spiritual visions. Plutarch, the great Greek historian,
said of Kyphi: "Its aromatic substances lull to sleep, allay anxieties and
brighten dreams. It is made of things that delight most in the night."
Kyphi is though to have been the world's first perfume. The only
surviving bottle was discovered in the tomb of Tutankhamun.
Remarkably, after 3,300 years it still had a perceptible odour.

Egyptian perfume was as fashionable in ancient Greece as French
perfume is now throughout the world. Although the art of making
perfumed oils for anointing the body and scenting the bath started in
Egypt, the Greeks and Romans raised it to an art form. Caligula spent

enormous sums on scented baths, for he believed that aromatic baths could restore a body jaded by sexual excesses.

Egyptian Baths

The ancient Egyptians considered bathing to be essential to their health and well-being, and often used aromatic oils and other fragrances in their baths. They were also the first to make soap from the soapwort plant. We all know that Cleopatra liked her baths and had a preference for ass's milk. However, the greatest advances in bathing were made by the Romans.

Roman Baths

To the ancient Romans, bathing was considered a ritual and a social affair, rather than a means to simply cleanse the body. Bathing was a communal experience that could last up to five hours. The famous themae, or baths, were based on the Egyptian precedents, and worked on the basis that bathers had to work up a sweat before being scrubbed and then soaking in hot and cold tubs.

Romans would first take a cool shower in the frigidarium a vast, vaulted room at the centre of the baths. This was followed by a massage and a succession of warm and hot baths (in the tepidarium and caldarium). Then it was back to the frigidarium for a final cold shower and invigorating rubdown.

At the peak of the Graeco-Roman civilization baths were celebrated for their majestic splendour and elegance. The finest craftsmen elegantly designed these grand bathing halls. They were inlaid with precious gems and metals dazzled the eye, great works of art were commission for statues of Hercules, the God of Strength, and Hygeia, the Goddess of health.

The overthrow of the Roman Empire in the 5th century and the growth of Christianity brought about a dramatic change in attitudes towards bathing. The barbarian tribes who conquered Rome found scented baths and the obsession with cleanliness incomprehensible. In addition, the Church disapproved of the decadence of the elaborate Roman bathing rituals. With bathhouses no longer deemed acceptable, many of the technologies instigated by the Romans disappeared. Europe was plunged back into its former grimy ways, and it was not until the 18th century that bathing became popular again.

Turkish Baths

When bathing Turkish style, the emphasis was on spiritual and physical rejuvenation. A few hours in the bathhouse or hamman helped to free the body of toxins, opened up the pores, cleansed the skin and supposedly cured diarrhoea, scabies, high fever, rheumatism, chronic depression and impotence. In harems women would join together to gossip, to bathe one another and to wash and comb each other's hair.

The Turks believed that the intense heat of the hamman enhanced fertility and if husbands denied their wives visits to the bath house, the women had grounds for divorce. The Turks believed that baths and a cleanly bathed body were vital to remain sexually potent. And regular baths would be part of any aphrodisiac regime. Important occasions, such as a newborn's fortieth day and weddings, were always celebrated at the hamman. These bathing establishments were originally complementary to mosques, but today they are still used as public bath houses.

Japanese Baths

The Japanese get clean to bathe. Ancient traditions made scrubbing and cleansing the skin a prerequisite before soaking in the hinolburo, a traditional Japanese bathtub. In comparison, the standard Western body wash is a superficial and perfunctory once over with soap, and not worth comparison.

But seeing as Japan is situated on volcanic islands with over 20,000 hot springs, it's not surprising that bathing has become such an art form. Bathing Japanese style in the communal hot springs, or onsens, was an holistic experience and a time to catch up with the family and friends, scrub backs and drink sake, whereas bathing at home in solitude was a time for contemplating, rebalancing, recovering vitality and a sense of well-being.

If the Egyptians were obsessed with personal hygiene, the Romans classed bathing as a ceremonial ritual, and to the Turks and the Japanese the bathhouse was a social and recreational centre, which was an indispensable part of daily life.

For centuries, people have taken to the waters in nature's own hot springs, in opulent marble bathhouses or in open-air bathtubs.

It was not until the advent of Christianity that dramatic changes occurred affecting both the social and beautifying benefits of bathing. Considered to be dangerously sensual and with the potential to lead the devout Christian astray, bathing became an act associated with licentiousness and eroticism and in many Western cultures was no longer favourable. But by the late 19th century, bathing slowly gained acceptance again when it was advised for hygienic reasons. Today, the sensual and physical pleasures of bathing are so appealing. It's essential to take time out to wallow in the tub and so improve the state of your mind, body and spirit.

Therapeutic baths

Soaking in a colour bath is a particularly pleasant and relaxing form of healing, this can take different forms, you can use dyes or food colourings (editor's note: test the bath and yourself for tendency to stains first!) to turn the water the colour that you want, but it you do not like the idea of this, you can add bath salts, flowers, flower essences, herbs or essential oils to the water. There are many different kinds of foam baths and bath gels, but most of these are synthetic and are sold for their scent alone. Some products contain essential oils, which are very beneficial because they are 100 per cent natural. They are not only absorbed through the skin, but the scent can be inhaled from the bath water.

If you add essential oils to a colour bath yourself remember that only a very few drops are used, so read the instruction on the bottle and follow them carefully.

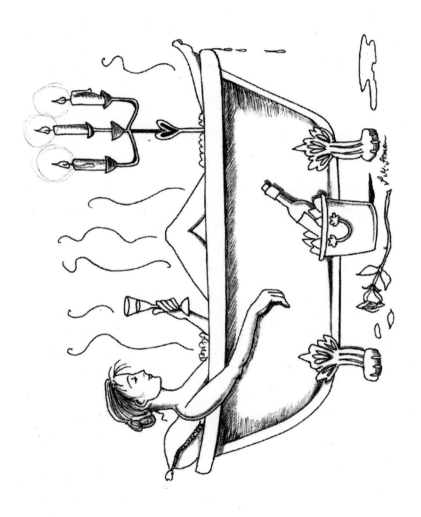

Fragrance with colour oils can also be added to salts for different combinations to relieve stress, clear the mind, or just to help you to feel good about yourself. The combination of fragrance with colour is especially healing and therapeutic if you select a particular flower essence for the effect it has on you. Use rose essential oil and add some rose petals and pink colour to your bath. Add some pink candles and the result will be heaven and a very good prelude to sexual intercourse.

An easy and cheap way to get the benefit of herbal baths is to use tea bags, brew up, for instance, a pot of Chamomile tea and add it to your bath water for a relaxing bath. Make sure that you will not be disturbed for half an hour, put on some music and revitalize your body and your mind.

Flower essences are made from flowers that have been energized by being placed in pure water and exposed to the direct light of the sun. they are then combined with alcohol to make a tincture. These are perhaps best known as the product sold as the Bach Flower Remedies named after Dr Edward Bach, their inventor.

When taking a colour bath, don't have the water too hot and add the essential oil (a maximum of 10 drops) and colour just before getting into the bath. You can alter the water temperature to match the mood; a cooling bath would be blue and the water would be cooler, but hot reviving water could be red or orange and the water would be hotter. But as a general rule a moderate temperature close to body temperature is best.

Colour Bath Guide
• A blue bath will help you unwind after a busy day and put your mind at rest, and with an indigo bath you can escape from the everyday world and it can also be aid mediation.

• Violet baths will inspire you to new heights of idealism in your life and your work. These baths are relaxing and are best later in the day

• For your morning bath chose colours such as yellow, orange and red to wake you and energize you for the day. Take care with red; however, as it is such a strong energy, red and orange would be good for cold winter mornings and to ward off colds and chills.

• If you are undecided or need to make a decision try a yellow bath, and add some rosemary essential oil to clear your mind.

• A green bath is a particularly appropriate one to take in the spring and summer, when you want to be in harmony with nature use with lavender oil or geranium oil for a fresh relaxing and revitalizing bath.

• A green bath with lavender can also help before bed to get you off to sleep. Other evening baths could include a blue bath with a few drops of patchouli oil to help you to reflect on your problems and come up with solutions to them.

• You can also clean your aura with a turquoise bath which is also good for the immune system add some sea salt and neroli or frankincense essential oil.

Moon Magic Bath

The effects of the moon on us as human beings has for many years been discussed and speculated upon, especially as far as the female gender is concerned. But what of the benefits of this magical event that occurs every 28 days? Centuries ago our forefathers embraced the moon and all its power, they recognised it for what it could do and paid homage to it. Also the moon and witchcraft always seem to go hand in hand, some authorities would have us believe that there are only negative aspects to this.

However there is a positive side too, I do know a few 'recipes' that are simple, yet very effective in helping to rejuvenate the mind, body and soul. I have advised clients to follow bath remedies with amazing results. This is merely a recipe handed down through the ages, on which our great-grandmothers would have used when they needed an extra boost, and one which is extremely satisfying for the soul.

Fill a pint container (it must be clear glass) with water and place it outside on the night of the full moon. (If you can't place it outside, then place it on a window sill inside.) The next night fill a bath with warm water, not too hot. Add the moon 'energised water. Also add some fresh leaves of basil, half a cup of milk, some salt, a few drops of wine and some rosewood essential oil. Rosewater, rose petals, or a pink bubble bath can be added. For an extra boost, add some candlelight, gentle music and sweet smelling incense. Now sink into this glorious bath, knowing that you are filling your body and soul with the powerful energy of the moon.

During this bath think about what you want in your life, to lose weight, overcome an illness, be successful in an endeavour, and find love or improve your sex life.

Bathing alone is luscious, but bathing with a partner can be very sensually arousing. Light the room with candlelight, use soft music, fragrances, and fresh flowers and relax. Rub each other down with a large fluffy towel and anoint each other with sweet smelling body lotion or aromatic oils afterwards.

Essential oils

Baths before bedtime with lavender, rose and chamomile oil really help you to relax and feel more sensitive. The sedative oils include Benzoin (use in very small dilution only 3 to 4 drops maximum) which can be very helpful with external worries that are often at the root of sleeplessness and sexual anxiety. Bergamot is a good choice where insomnia is linked with depression, frigidity and lack of interest in sex.

A hot footbath before bed also helps relaxation. You can use 4 drops of Peppermint or Lavender oil to relieve tired feet then if you can get your partner to give you a foot rub even better. Or follow the bath with a loving massage with essential oils.

By choosing essences of lavender, bergamot, neroli or geranium you can nourish the very cells of the body while melting away the tension of the day; to enliven a tired body for a night of passion use rosemary, ylang ylang, clary sage, niaouli or lemon.

Goddess of Perfumes and Nature. Aphrodite de Capri in the cliff gardens on Capri

Chapter 13
The Goddess Within

hroughout time and history Gods and Goddesses of erotic love have inspired humans with their awesome presence through dance and song, music and food, perfumes and oils, and feasts and celebration to honour life's sacred sensuality.

Female sexuality has been embodied by courtesans, geishas and prostitutes. These women were well educated and held in high esteem in the community. Many of them lived, worked, danced, were talented musicians and tended the temple. They served the community and represented the goddess of love. In some cultures each woman in the community did her time as a sacred prostitute at the temple in honour and respect of the high goddess. The meaning of prostitute was 'one who stood on behalf of' or represented the great goddess. From the goddess the essence of feminine power flowed and the temple prostitute celebrated her own beauty and sexuality while serving the populace. I believe that within every one of us is a goddess or a god, even if only in the bedroom.

In Tantra you discover that by honouring the god or goddess in yourself and in your partner you can see beyond the limitation of personality and see the divine in the other person, and perceive the same potential in yourself.

In the book *The Goddess Within*, psychologists Jennifer and Roger Woolger attribute different attributes to the six major goddesses. Demeter, the nurturer; Hera the power seeker; Athena, the wise and confident career woman; Artemis, the lover of nature and freedom;

Persephone the intuitive, psychic, sensitive aspect of the woman; and of course Aphrodite the goddess of love, ruler over sensuality, the arts and beauty in all things.

I have below outlined some of the major sexual gods and goddesses but there are many more from all over the world. Ffind a meaningful one from below or seek out your own.

Aphrodite

Aphrodite particularly interests us as she is the goddess governing perfumery, sensuality, massage, cosmetics and all things aesthetic and pleasurable. Aphrodite, born from the foam of the sea, is well known as the Greek goddess of love, and is often seen crowned in spring blossoms. She is always associated with desire, seduction, sexual love and ecstasy and she wore a magic girdle that was reputed to cause those who saw her to fall in love with her instantly. The dove and the dolphin, apples, roses, myrtle, lilies, fennel and opium poppies are all associated with the goddess and held sacred.

The Goddess Aphrodite arose from the waves and realizing her nakedness, plucked some sprigs from a myrtle bush to cover herself. This is why it is said the myrtle plant has leaves shaped like a vagina, the outer lips (*labia majora*) being likened to the lips of the myrtle, and inner (*labia minora*) to the fruit of the myrtle.

Aphrodite was worshipped as the goddess of love, beauty, sexuality and passion; she ruled all things sensual, including the knowledge of the sexual uses of aromatic plants. From her name we have the word aphrodisiac; from her son's name Eros, from a love affair with Zeus, gives us erotic.

Also according to Greek legend, the art of perfumery came to mortals when Aphrodite's handmaiden, Oenone, confided in her lover, Paris. Paris after anointed himself with aromatics, managed to steal Helen of Troy away from her husband, Menelaus. Later, when Helen returned to Greece she spread the knowledge of perfumery.

Aphrodite could be cruel; when the women of Lemnos refused to pay homage to her she cursed them with a foul smell which made their husbands reject them.

Apollo

The Greek god Apollo representing life, immortality, harmonious balance, beauty and goodness. He could be considered to be the male version of Aphrodite. Apollo was the son of Zeus and the Titaness Leto and the twin brother of the goddess Artemis the virgin huntress. He was one of the most important deities of both the Greek and Roman religions, the sun god, god of prophecy, archery and music.

Apsaras

The Apsaras were formerly human women, priestesses of the sacred sexual rites in 12th century Asia. They were also known as 'Daughters of Pleasure'. These women were educated and intelligent, they were gifted musicians and they took many lovers, both human and divine. According to ancient literature, they wore marvellous headdresses and stunning, sensual garments, and garlanded themselves with aromatic flowers as they danced, and sang, played their music and celebrated sensual life; the original hedonists?

Artemis

Artemis was the twin sister of Apollo, the Greek god of the sun; she is the Goddess of chastity, virginity, the hunt and the moon and nature. But because of her connection with the hunt she is more active than Aphrodite in seeking love, or perhaps encouraging a reluctant lover of either sex and for winning love under difficult circumstances. She is perfect for outdoor love spells.

Bacchus

The Roman feasts in honour of Bacchus, god of wine and lust, were elaborate occasions, with roses being as important a commodity as wine, women, and rich food. The Romans were obsessed by the rose; rose water perfumed the public baths, flowed from fountains in the emperor's palaces, and were strewn everywhere at banquets. Even wine was rose scented and the cure for the overindulgent.

Cernunnos

Stone carvings have been found over doorways through out Celtic counties, symbolising man's relations with the sacredness of Mother Nature. Cernunnos was the Celtic horned god and stag of the forest and was the consort of the moon. He was half man and half stag, sporting antlers and celebrating his strength and virility as he protected the honoured nature of the greenwood.

Bull gods, Apis of Egypt, half man and half bull, have long been noted for their connection with celestial and earthly influence.

Diana

Diana is the Roman counterpart of Artemis and because of her strong association with the moon in all its phases is the Goddess of fertility as well as love. Like Artemis, she is Goddess of the hunt and a virgin goddess, but is often invoked in her role of earth goddess and protector of women in childbirth. She was renowned for her beauty and represented spiritual love.

Dionysus

In Greek mythology, Dionysus's totem was a panther and he carried a phallic sceptre topped with a pinecone. Dionysus is also celebrated with Bacchus, Adonis and Pan. Dionysus is renowned for lusty bacchanalian festivals in honour of the god of the grape harvest and the drinking of the sacred wine. There would be dancing with satyrs and beautiful woman clad in gowns and animal skins, while men wore garlands of grapevines. These orgies of food and wine would go on for days; this harvest festival was a celebration of the good things in life.

Ephesus

Ephesus was the ancient goddess of fertility, sexuality and nourishment, also known as Diana of Ephesus; she was worshipped in the Near East and Greece, especially in Anatolia. She was many breasted and a potent fertility symbol with many layers of her skirt that represented the animal, plant and mineral kingdoms.

Eros

For many, Eros symbolizes our deepest sensuality, and the sexually erotic side of spring. In Roman mythology, Eros was represented as a beautiful, androgynous youth, who was transformed into the god of love; his purpose was to seduce all creatures, male and female alike. Eros was born of Mother Nature, and represents the frippery of desire and of love and lust.

Hathor

Hathor was the Ancient Egyptian Goddess of lovers and love itself; couples would call on her as a powerful fertility goddess and protector of women. She was also worshipped as a sky goddess, Hathor is often shown wearing a sun disk between the horns of a cow as a crown. She is a Goddess of joy, art, music and dance and was trusted to the sacred eye of Ra the Sun God, through which she could see all things. She is often invoked in sex/love magic because of her link with the eye of truth and with harmony. The love she inspires is noble and dignified, her patronage will strengthen a relationship.

Ishtar-Inanna

In Babylonian times, the Goddess Ishtar was known as the 'Queen of Heaven'. She stood poised, holding her breasts forward as an offering; she was also known an 'Inanna' in ancient Sumeria. Her consort Damuzi inspired her to write erotic love poetry. She rejoiced in her sexuality and opened the portal of heaven through the prostitution of her priestesses, who were known as Ishtaritu or 'Joy Maidens'. Through sexual union they bestowed her divine influence on those who sought her blessing; using acts of sexual pleasure and ritual. She appears in the bible as 'Anath', 'Ashtoreth', or 'Asherah', and as 'Astarte' and 'Mari' in the Near East. She has been known as 'the Light of the World', 'the Great Whore', 'Mother of Harlots', and 'Babylon the Great'.

Mary Magdalene

Wife of Christ or sacred harlot and funerary priestess? She was also known as 'the woman who knew all' and 'the woman with the alabaster jar'. The Magdalene means 'she of the temple tower', the magdalene and her women, priestesses of the temple, financially supported Jesus and the apostles. The magdalenes anointed the feet of Christ with fragrant oils.

A sacred brothel in Rome was established by Pope Julius 11 and provided for the Holy sisters of the Order of St Mary Magdalene, also known as the magdalenes, or sacred whores.

Nymphs
As symbols of the provocation of sexual enjoyment, in Greek mythology the nymphs roamed the streams and forests, in search of handsome youths to favour with their embraces, sometime even the wild satyrs of the woods won their favours.

Oshun
Honey is the favourite offering to Oshun; she was an African goddess of love and the River Goddess of Fertility. She would wear yellow scarves around her waist, peacock feathers in her hair and her breasts would be naked and smeared with honey.

Bells and fans, water plants and animals were sacred to her. She is sometimes depicted as a mermaid with two tails and she could divine the future from sea shells.

Pan
Pan is the oldest of the Greek gods, and was also known as the 'king of the satyrs' hoofed and horned, half man half goat. Pan breathes the fresh spring air and couples with water nymphs by a lake during the feasts of Dionysus.

Sappho
According to Greek mythology, Sappho lived in 6000 BCE; she was a female lyricist and lived on the Greek island of Lesbos. She was the archetypal lesbian and wrote erotic poetry and songs proclaiming the beauty of woman.

Venus
The Roman goddess of love and sensuality was called Venus, and she too was supposed to have been born from the sea and to have covered

136

her nakedness with myrtle leaves. The evening star is named after her and temples were dedicated to her, schools of instruction in sexual techniques were taught by Venerri or harlot priestesses.

The Three Graces in attendance on Venus and her son, Cupid, were crowned with Myrtle leaves; when accompanying the Muses however they wore wreaths of rose. Rose essence has been called the 'blood of Venus' and Roman temples were always adorned with rose. Venus gave us the word venery, meaning sexual desire, and venereal of the sexual organs, and it is not a coincident that Venice is called 'city of lovers.'

Chapter 14

Massage and Aromatherapy

n this chapter I have tried to present some practical tips and recipes and alternative methods of treating sexual problems as well as offering a brief history of the erotic use of aromatics in ancient times. The way to become the ideal lover is to be beautiful from the inside out and allowing aromatic essences to make you feel attractive and sensual is a step in the right direction.

Scented bed clothes can be extremely sensual and very personal. You can spray hydrosols of your choice, the best being neroli or ylang-ylang for a sexy mood. But to aid tranquillity and restful sleep use lavender or sweet marjoram.

There are a number of ways of scenting a bedroom; one method would be to use an electrically heated diffuser into which you drop the essential oil of your choice of rose, geranium, jasmin, myrtle, or whatever oil you choose. Candlelit fragrancers are also popular, but you could also drop a few drops of essential oil in a bowl of hot water and put it on your radiator.

The empress Josephine had a much more long-lasting method of scenting her bedroom; she had its walls impregnated with musk. Some say that if you visit her apartments you can still smell the musk in the air.

The Emperor Nero had a flamboyant taste for perfumes and had sprinklers in his apartment to spray his guests. At Roman orgies the smells of the foods and aromatics intensified the mood and the sensual delights for the participants and the onlookers. Aromatherapy can help you to get and stay in touch with this element of your psyche; oils such as rose or myrtle can also help you to identify with the goddess within.

Massage

Massage is a wonderful way of being physically close to someone allowing your loving energy to flow through your hands into your partner's body.

Sigmund Freud recognized that the important things in life are love and work; by massaging your partner one may say you are combining the two.

Massage is an excellent way to get to know your lover's body. Your skin is designed to process sensation and when we speak of something 'touching our heart' it is more than a metaphor. Your skin really does speak to your heart. When massaging your lover you are also communicating with them physically and spiritually.

Massage is a wonderful skill to learn, take a course, the nicest way to learn is to do a weekend course with your partner or a friend, and it also gives you someone to practice on. The ultimate sensual massage has to be the full body massage reputed to be so popular in Bangkok brothels. For this massage both partners have to be naked. Scented oil is then applied to your front and your lovers back with your partner lying face down. You straddle their body and lean forwards using your body to massage your partner's body; in this massage you do not use your hands. Your partner can then turn over and you massage the front of his/her body in the same ways. This can be a very sensual experience. Massage can be stimulating, highly erotic but it can also be tender, nurturing and soothing, promoting relaxation and restful sleep. For a loving couple massage is a natural way of communicating as well as being a basic tool of the art of love.

Aromatherapy

Aromatherapy uses the essential oils of plants to heal and beautify the body. Connected to herbal medicine but having its own separate identity, aromatherapy takes aromatic plant matter such as lavender and frankincense and distills its essence, and then it uses this essence in numerous beneficial ways.

The awareness of smell is very invigorating and stimulating and has been used for thousands of years. Aromatherapy was widely practised in Ancient India, Greece, Rome and Egypt. One of it most famous protagonists Cleopatra, perfumed her body with rose, frankincense and myrrh to lure both Julius Caesar and Mark Anthony into her bed. She also drenched the sails of her ship with rose or jasmin oil so lovers could anticipate her floral arrival from afar. One legend says that when she first met Mark Anthony she was knee deep in rose petals.

The word aromatherapy may have been coined in the twentieth century, but the use of aromatic oils and unguent for religious and sexual purposes goes back thousands of years to the dawn of civilization.

It is difficult to pinpoint which civilization first had the knowledge of perfumery and aromatherapy; the ancient Chinese say that the Yellow emperor first brought medicine and perfumes to the world, while in India the birth of perfumery is attributed to the god Indra.

Wherever aromatic plants were grown, people recognised their contribution to sexual and religious ecstasy and realizing the value of these commodities, they travelled to other lands to trade, selling the aromatic plants that grew in their own land and buy aromatics and herbs from other lands, in this way the knowledge spread. Today, modern women have professionally blended perfumes to dab behind their ears and on their bodies, in fact where ever they want to be kissed. Many men also use scented colognes and aftershaves to give their sex appeal a boost.

Every day we breathe over 23,000 times, bringing up to 10,000 different aromatic chemicals towards receptors at the top of our noses.

Their aromas are detected by hair like nerve ending that, unlike those involved in other senses, are directly connected to your brains. Messages are passed directly to the limbic system without first being filtered by higher centres. Many aromatic plants mimic closely the aroma of the sexual secretions of the human body and can stimulate your natural hormones and pheromones. Smells therefore have a profound effect on behaviour as they can trigger primitive responses that have not been modified by intellectual input. The limbic system is one of the most ancient parts of the brain and is linked to other nerve centres concerned with learning, memories, arousal, emotion and even hormone secretion. Smell can therefore evoke powerful responses such as hunger, nostalgia, fear and not least, sexual desire.

Interestingly, the sense of smell is more acute in women than men, and is strongest around the time of ovulation. In one study, women rated smell as one of the most important factors when choosing a mate, men however considered smell and looks as being evenly important when selecting a lover.

Low sex drive can respond to aromatherapy in many different ways including:

• To calm, relieve stress and relax

• Mimic the effect of natural pheromones

• Stimulate secretion of pheromones

• Stimulate erotic centres in the brain evoking desire

• Release inhibitions

• Have an oestrogen like effect

• Have a testosterone effect

You can therefore use aromatherapy oils to boost sex drive in both men and women.

When choosing aromatherapy oils it is essential to choose ones that both you and your partner like. Aromatherapy used a variety of techniques to obtain therapeutic benefit from essential oils. They may be inhaled, massaged into the skin, added to bath water, or heated in a variety of ways to perfume the atmosphere and produce an ambience.

Oils that come into contact with skin will be absorbed to some extent and will also have medicinal effect in the body. They can also cause irritation and should always be diluted with carrier oil. Never rub even well diluted essential oil into the genitals.

The following essential oils have properties that may help to boost sex drive. Cedarwood, cinnamon, cloves, jasmine, neroli, patchouli, rose, sandalwood and ylang-ylang. Rose petals, (modern equivalent is confetti), are strewn on the marriage bed in many cultures including the Roman and today's' tradition of throwing flower petals at marriages comes from this tradition.

The majority of essential oils are powerful and persistent so should be used sparingly. Do not use aromatherapy essential oils during pregnancy except under the advice of a qualified aromatherapist. There are several good books that will give you tips and massage routines and teach you the safe way to use essential oils. Never use high doses of essential oils without taking the utmost care; it is better to buy ready made mixes, which are readily available. Most essential oils work best in low dilutions and average mix would be 3-5 drops of essential oil to 5 ml of pure vegetable oil such as sweet almond. One of the most important oils is the precious sandalwood. Often used for its erotic properties, it can safely be used, for massaging even the most intimate area of the body when properly diluted.

Essential oils for massage are now widely available to the public via mail order or retail shops. Many oils are best used in a low dilution, for example ylang-ylang is very effective if used with caution but over do it and you will feel heavy, lethargic and headachy. (2 drops of ylang-ylang to 5 ml of oil is sufficient or 5 drops in an average size bath.

The History of Aromatherapy

The Hindu God Indra is always represented with his breast tinged with sandalwood. Sex and aromatherapy have married together perfectly. Imagine how even thousands of years ago, lovers rubbed scented oils into each other's bodies, experiencing the fulfilment of all their senses. The sense of smell delighted in the breathtaking perfumes of natural essences intermingling with their own body's aroma. Their sense of touch revelling in the feeling of massaging their loved one or by being massaged by them in return; their eyes beheld the erotic sight of oil glistening on their naked skin. My ex husband always used to say that his favourite colour on me was wet or soaked in oil.

Aromatherapy can also help bring about a peaceful state of mind, which in itself can bring harmony to a relationship. Many Eastern texts, when referring to mediation, stress the importance of deep breathing, they say that the mind follows the breath. It is from India as well as from China, that the ancient Egyptians obtained their knowledge and their supplies of many aromatic herbs. The Egyptians were the inventors of the public baths, later borrowed by the Romans and claimed as their own invention.

The passion for perfumes continued to intensify in Egypt until the time of Cleopatra, when it can be said to have reached its peak. Queen Cleopatra used aromatics in a lavish and extravagant way, which may have been a contributing factor to her active sex life. As well as being lover to Julius Caesar and Mark Anthony, she is said, according to legend, to have taken many lovers and to have fellated 100 centurions in a single day! Certainly she was no novice in the art of seduction: when summoned by Mark Anthony to meet him on the banks of the Tiber, she drenched the sails of her barge with rose and jasmin oils. Having sailed to where he waited, she invited Mark Anthony on board. "The very winds were lovesick." Shakespeare writes in his play *Anthony and Cleopatra*. There is no doubt that Mark Anthony was lost and spellbound with lust for the Egyptian queen.

In the Old Testament the Queen of Sheba and King Solomon act out their erotic and aromatic fantasy: "My lover has the scent of myrrh, he shall lie all night on my breast." Other known aphrodisiacs are mentioned in Proverbs: "I have perfumed my bed with myrrh, aloes and cinnamon."

The Romans knew that scents and perfumes possessed medicinal properties, and the most popular recipes were inscribed on marble tablets in the temple of Venus. Brides to be in the 4th century BCE were anointed with aromatic oils prior to their wedding. The Romans loved their public baths, and would daily visit the public baths and be bathed and anointed with aromatic oils while also exchanging gossip. Ovid, the great poet of the time of Emperor Augustus, told the Romans, "Adonis is a woodland boy, but became the darling of Venus". Was it because he smelled so good? We all know the saying "she/he smells good enough to eat". Nero's wife Poppaea is said to have bathed in ass's milk as did Queen Cleopatra, Poppaea was a poet and wrote, "Wives are out of fashion now, mistresses are in, rose leaves are dated; now cinnamon's the thing".

At the traditional Roman orgy, of eating, drinking, bathing and copulating, the genitals were actually adored. One month in every year male genitals were worshipped in honour of the god Liber. The month of this phallic worship corresponds to the time of Libra. Romans worshipped the genitals as the gateway to immortality and believed that you could become one with the gods by reaching sexual ecstasy; as is believe by those practicing the Indian Tantra.

In the East the Harem women relied heavily on the use of aromatic for their beauty and the power to increase sexual power. Bathing was not only a necessary obligation but the main social event of the day. It would last several hours and the cosseted women and sometimes neutered males, would be oiled, depilated of hair, beautified waiting for the sexual whim of the sultan.

Catherine de Medici adored aromatics, especially neroli, which she transplanted from her native Italy to the south of France when she became wife of Henry 11. The Empress Josephine loved scents, and being a Creole brought up in Martinique she was used to wearing oils and creams of almond and coconut imbued with heady aromas from

144

jasmine and other heavily scented flowers. She was fanatical about the use of aromatics and impregnated the walls of her bedroom with musk. Her favourite flower was the violet. Napoleon gave her instructions to wear only orange water, lavender water, and eau de Cologne when she visited him on location, claiming that her perfumes distracted him to such an extent that he could not concentrate on planning his battles. But when they had been apart for a lengthy period he would send word to her 'Je reviens en trois jours, ne te laves pas' (I will return in three days, don't wash), so potent did he find her natural body odours. When Josephine died Napoleon had violets planted on her grave and in loving memory of their nights of passion together he would always wear a pressed violet in the gold locket around his neck.

The use of aromatics for seduction became so rife in Europe that the English Parliament of 1770 even passed an act intended to protect men form being beguiled into marriage. "All women, of whatever age... that shall from and after such act, impose upon seduce and betray in matrimony, any of his subjects, by the use of scents, paints, cosmetics... shall incur the penalty of the laws in force against witchcraft and like misdemeanours..," Women in Senegal used the tubers of the ginger plant to make belts, with the aim of arousing the dormant senses of their men.

The Queen of Sheba had a famous love affair with King Solomon. Sheba, also sometimes known as Punt, which was a land of many aromatic plants. The Queen traded aromatic substances with King Solomon, and before returning to her own land she and King Solomon consummated their relationship many times.

Recipes for Aromatherapy

When putting essential oils into a bath, add the essential oils to a little base oil (sweet almond or any pure vegetable oil) or milk and put the mixture into the bath when the bath is ready, not while the water is running.

Massage blends for baths
For depression and sexual tension
4 drops ylang-ylang, 4 drops lavender

For restless legs syndrome at night
4 drops bergamot, 4 drops chamomile (Roman), 4 drops lavender

For restlessness and too active brain
5 drops frankincense, 5 drops lavender

For winter blues (SAD)
5 drops grapefruit, 5 drops lavender,   2 drops rose

For menstrual or hormonal problems
4 drops clary sage, 4 drops lavender, 2 drops rose
  Or
4 drops clary sage, 2 drops ylang-ylang, 2 drops chamomile (R)

For painful memories and worries
8 drops frankincense
  Or
5 drops frankincense, 3 drops grapefruit, 2 drops neroli

Insomnia disturbed sleep and nightmares
5 drops lavender, 3 drops chamomile (R), 4 drops mandarin
  Or
5 drops Frankincense, 5 drops lavender.

Lying awake with worry or anxiety
5 drops chamomile (R), 2 drops lemon, 3 drops lavender

For aphrodisiac, sensual and relaxing
6 drops ylang-ylang, 2 grapefruit
  Or
4 drops ylang-ylang, 4 drops sandalwood, 2 drops jasmine
  Or
4 drops rose, 4 drops lavender, 4 drops of frankincense

For a stimulating aphrodisiac tonic
5 drops clary sage, 5 drops patchouli

Reflexology

A foot massage can be very sensual and energizing to the sexual organs; and reflexology has long been used for the symptoms of sexual dysfunction and can help men with premature ejaculation, impotence and loss of interest in sex. For women reflexology is very helpful for fertility and sexual problems. It is also an ideal treatment for menstrual and hormonal problems.

Interestingly the points around the ankle below the ankle bones and the heel correspond to the genital area, and the heel points correspond to Achilles' vulnerable spot according the Homer's *Iliad*, Achilles was the son of Thetis, a sea goddess. When he was born, his mother dipped Achilles into the blessed river Styx, which conferred invulnerability, but the spot on his heel where her fingers held him was not exposed to the magical waters and he was therefore vulnerable in this area. That is why we now describe weakness of vulnerability in ourselves as our Achilles' heel.

Hand reflexology can be done anywhere, and holding hands is a great part of romantic courtship in most cultures. Ear reflexology also known as auriculotherapy is widely practised in China and other Far Eastern countries. It was instigated a long time ago when it was observed that the shape of the ear corresponded to a body curled up in the fetal position, and that points on the ear corresponded to parts of the human body.

For a man who has been impotent for some time, it may be beneficial to practice penis reflexology each day as well as taking aromatic baths and massages. Reflexology of the penis is a little-known therapy outside of Taoist love practises and although at present unproven in the West, it would seem of offer a novel and pleasurable way to treat sexual problems.

Just as there are reflex zones on the hands, feet, and ears, so too on the penis we can find reflexes to the body's internal organs and hormonal system. Use the thumb and fingers, work using small circular motions along the shaft of the penis, from the head to the tip and back again. Mantak Chia, Taoist secret of love, also asserts that to massage the head of the penis along the prostrate reflex is beneficial to the prostate and that regular massage can act as a prostate gland cancer preventive.

Chapter 15
Special Place

Illusion is the first of all pleasures

Oscar Wilde.

t is vital to take time out of the ordinary everyday routine to create a nurturing, sensual space to make love to your partner. This can be achieved in many different ways; you can put together your own pleasure zone. Take the phone off the hook, send the children to the grandparents or forbid them to interrupt unless the house is burning down. This pleasure zone can be your bedroom but it could just as easily be a moonlit glade, or a blanket decorated with candles, not in January I suspect, just make sure it is a place where you can relax and will not be disturbed.

Invite your partner to a midnight rendezvous in your living room, or the gazebo, supply some strawberries and cream, candles and romantic music. Use your imagination and create your own harem fantasy. Use all the senses, smell, sight, sound, taste and touch in your fantasy; sometimes a blindfold will heighten the sensual delights. Cover the bed with rose petals and burn some essential oils mix with candles and sweet music. Food like chocolate, pieces of fruit are good and dress up or down; use silks or leather what ever turns you on. Tell stories, share fantasies, watch pornography, act out fantasies; but be safe - sexual experience must be a shared experience, never force your partner to participate in anything sexual or otherwise that they are not comfortable with. Many couples enjoy sado-masochistic activities but there should always be a safety word that will halt things if they become uncomfortable or disagreeable for either partner.

You can send your partner sexy messages, tell them what you want to do to them when you get them alone on Saturday night, anticipation is a strong aphrodisiac.

Lighting
The importance of lighting is vital as it can change the whole atmosphere of a sexual event. There are times when you want a bright vibrant atmosphere, but usually a subdued lighting scheme is most appropriate. You can place aromatic candles around the room in candle sticks or use small night lights. Your can use dimmed lights, coloured bulbs or just a table lamp with a low bulb or coloured shade.

Temperature
Keep your room warm and comfortable, but not too hot. If venturing outside choose clement weather although having sex wearing nothing but a fur coat and thigh length boots may well be someone's idea of heaven.

Foods
It can be very sensual to have a tray with exotic foods and nibbles, as well as something to drink. Snacking can be revitalizing during a passionate evening. Some good foods can be found in the A-Z of aphrodisiacs; but chocolate, nuts, fruit and cream, as well as delicious pastries are always good. And don't forget the presentation, beautiful crystal goblets and special china.

Accessories
Here you can let your imagination run riot, but they could include features, flowers, silky material, sexy lingerie, and jewellery. Men and women can experiment with different hair styles and makeup and clothing. Let the goddess out by emphasising your eyes. Makeup is not limited to the face, rouge those nipples; you can buy body makeup or use chocolate to decorate your body or that of your partner; it is great fun licking it off afterwards or as part of your love play.

You can use crystals and perhaps a god and goddess statue that seems to represent the male and female principle for you. In same sex relationships you still need the two foci; these can be Sappho and Diana

151

for lesbian and Apollo and Eros for the male homosexual couples or any item that have a special meaning to you, such as shells from the beach where you met or an item that has a special meaning to you as a couple.

Music
Music is very important. Select soft gentle music for romantic gentle sex and more rousing music for energetic sex; we all have some music that is meaningful to us.

Sex Toys
There are many sex toys available, from vibrators to handcuffs to sexy underwear. Some people even have their own dungeon or harem room in their house; let your imagination run riot, experiment and have fun but, be safe. You can even buy sex toys in Tescos these days.

Sexual Fantasies
Give yourself and your partner permission to relate your sexual fantasies; and to perhaps play one out. Sharing does not imply any demand or need to act out a particular fantasy. You are both free to do whatever you want about them. Give each other support, and don't be afraid to go into elaborate detail, the relating of the fantasy can be as exciting as the act itself. There can be a feeling of relief and humour and the realization that we all have our fantasies no matter how bizarre some of these dreams and fantasies can be. Some people say that they do not have sexual dreams or fantasies but we all have a secret dream of some sort. This can also include looking at sexy magazines or watching adult movies, what is important is that you share with your partner without judgement.

Love and understanding is the key, be supportive and broadminded and don't be afraid to try something different now and again.

Chapter 16

A-Z of Aphrodisiacs

Absinthe
(Artemisia Absinthiumm) Absinthe is a liqueur made in France, which is manufactured from a bushy plant with silky stems and small yellow flowers. It is a green liqueur compounded of marjoram, oil of aniseed and other aromatic oils. *Aremisia absinthiumm* known as wormwood was used anciently to banish demons. Hence it was associated with the rites of St John's Eve, when a crown of the plant was made from its sprays for apotropaic purposes to protect against evil spirits. Although absinthe has been considered a sexual stimulant, when taken in large quantities it leads to impotence and insanity. (Also see Wormwood)

Abuta
(Chondrodendron tomentosum, Cissampelos pareira; Perieria brava) Abuta is a beautiful woody vine also known as 'ice vine' or 'velvet leaf,' which climbs high over trees in the West Indies, and South America. The dried root and bark are taken orally and contain a variety of isoquinoline alkaloids that have great benefit for all with low sex drive, menstruation and childbirth problems. In Ecuador it is called the 'midwife herb' and is reputed to reawaken an interest in sex after childbirth.

Acorus Calamus

(Acorus Calamus) An aromatic herb ruled by Venus was called Sweet Flag in the Middle Ages. In ancient Roman days it was considered an aphrodisiac and associated with many erotic practices. It was known as the Venus plant. (Also see sweet flag)

Adrenaline

This drug is often used in treating asthma, is said to have occasional aphrodisiac effects. This is also the case with the other drugs that stimulate the sympathetic nervous system, ephedrine and amphetamine sulphate or Benzedrine. These drugs, however, should never be used without medical supervision.

Affion

This was a Chinese preparation, of which the chief ingredient was opium. It was asserted that its erotic effect was intense and violent. (See Opium)

Agate

Like many other stones, precious and semiprecious, the agate has a putative reputation for stimulating amorous activity. In the Middle Ages in particular great trust was placed in the efficacy of such stones, in the sense that they possess talismanic virtues and was often used in love spells.

Agave

(Agave Americana) Agave is found in Central and South America and there are a number of different species, one large leafed variety 'a sisalana' is suitable for obtaining a fibre known as sisal kemp. In Mexico they add the seeds of the thorn apple 'datura' or the 'ololiuqui vine' Turbina corymbosa to the drink. Tequila is distilled from *Agave tequilana*; other species are used to making a schnapps called mescal. In Oaxaca, a grub (gusano) that lives in the agave stalk is often added to the beverage; this is said to increase sexual desire. It was widely used in Columbian times, as a medicine and in religious ceremonies and as a tea to increase sexual desire.

Agnus Castus

(Vitex Chaste Berry) Agnus Castus also called the 'chaste tree' and 'Abraham's Balm' whose leaves were anciently reputed to produce an anti-aphrodisiac effect. Pliny the Elder, the Roman author of the Historia Naturalis and Dioscorides, the first century A.D. Greek army physician, author of *Materia Medica*, mentions that during a certain

Greek festival called the Thesmophoria, agnus was strewn over the bed by married women. The thistle was also reputed to have this anti aphrodisiac property. A 13th century polymath, Arnaud de Villeneuve, asserted that the mere possession of an article fashioned from the wood of agnus castus produced an anti-aphrodisiac effect.

Alcohol

Alcohol, with sugar added, was used to promote the amorous feelings of King Louis XIV. In some European countries it was a folk custom to offer a bride and bridegroom cakes moistened with sugar, or honey, and alcohol. Francis 1 of France was also known for his cultivated tastes, and for his sexual prowess, he often used aphrodisiac drinks and foods. He was notorious for the number of his lovers; but he died of exhaustion from his excesses. In small amounts, alcohol removes inhibitions by depressing the 'higher centres' of the brain. Sexual desire may be increased but the consummation is often negligible or abortive. In large amounts alcohol will cause impotence.

Alstonia

(Alstonia scholaris) This tree is sometimes called 'dita', 'bitter bark', 'devil's tree', 'pale mara' and 'chatim'. It grows in the rain forests of India, Ceylon and Borneo. The dita tree has white, funnel-shaped flowers. The bark has, in the past, been used as parchment by Asian scholars, leading to the name scholaris. The bark and seeds have also been used in Asian folk medicine for centuries. A tea is used for menstrual cramps; there are no proven aphrodisiac qualities but myth has it that it can prolong an erection and delay orgasm; it acts as a general tonic and mild stimulant.

Almonds

An aphrodisiac preparation described by Nefzawi in the Perfumed Garden says: "*Take a glassful of very thick honey, eat twenty almonds and one hundred grains of the pine tree before bedtime, and continue for three days.*" (See Almond soup)

Ambergris

Ambergris is a waxy substance found in tropical seas, believed to be the secretion in the intestines of the sperm whale; it was used in cooking as an aphrodisiac. In 17th century France courtiers and roués customarily nibbled chocolates covered with ambergris. Madam du Barry used ambergris as a perfume to retain the affection of Louis XV. In the Orient, ambergris is still considered as a potent aphrodisiac. Coffee is often served with a little ambergris at the bottom of the cup. According to one authority, three grains of ambergris are sufficient to produce lustful desires and to restore fatigue of old age or of over-indulgence. Among the Persians, pastilles consisting of powdered ambergris, rubies, gold, and pearls were eaten as an aphrodisiac.

American Ginseng

(Panax quinquefolius) American ginseng is a direct relation of the Manchurian ginseng root. It is a robust, larger variety; used by the North American Indians' medicine men as a medicine and for its aphrodisiac effects. The root was often used as a protective magical amulet and as a love charm.

Anacyclus Pyrethrum

The plant *Anacyclus pyrethrum* is also called 'Pellitory' in Spain, it is used medicinally, but according to a famous Arab erotologist also has aphrodisiac properties.

Anchovies

In many Southern European countries anchovies have been reputed to be lust provoking.

Angel Water

Angel water was used by the Portuguese and was popular in the 18th century. To make it you shake together a 1/2 litre of orange flower water, a 1/2 litre of rose water, a 1/4 litre myrtle water and add two thirds of distilled spirit of musk, and two thirds of spirit of ambergris. It is reputed to be a powerful aphrodisiacal aid.

Angel's Trumpet

(Brugmansia auarea) There are several species of angel's trumpet or 'tree datura' that grow in South America and other tropical areas. The angel's trumpet is a well known Indian medicinal plant and is used by shamans as a hallucinogen. It is reputed to be a powerful aphrodisiac and stimulant.

Aniseed *(Pimpinella Anisum)* The anis bush grows in the Mediterranean region and has a long history of uses as a spice and medicinal fruit. Aniseed and Star Anise are both gently stimulating aphrodisiacs that were used powdered and combined with honey to form an aphrodisiac paste. This was applied to the genitals in Ancient

156

India for an explosive effect. Aniseed was also a central ingredient of the rich, spicy cake served at Roman weddings to encourage the sex drive of newly weds. In the famous Hindu guide to erotology, the *Ananga Ranga* in respect of phallic effectiveness applications are advised that include anise, honey, leaves of the jai, rui seed, Hungarian grass and lotus flower pollen. Anise was known to Dioscorides, the ancient Greek botanist both in European and in Arab counties. During the Middle Ages anise has had a wide amatory reputation.

Annatto

(Bixa orellana) Annatto is a small tree native to Southern and Central America and the Caribbean. It has heart-shaped pods that contain seeds and a mature tree can produce 600 pounds of seeds. In Colombia and Mexico the leaves of the annatto tree are a valued aphrodisiac and are used to make a love tea. The pods are also decorated and used as a talisman.

Ants

A medieval aphrodisiac recipe that appears in Sinibaldus, Benedict Sinibaldus, an Italian professor of medicine, who published a book in Rome in 1642, contained dried black ants. Oil was poured over them and they were enclosed in a glass jar, ready for use. Winged ants were used medicinally during the Renaissance and were often substituted for cantharides. I am not sure what you did with them.

Anvalli Anvalli is a sexual stimulant mentioned in the Hindu erotic manuals Ananga Ranga. It consists of the outer shell of anvalli nuts, from which the juice is extracted. Dried in the sun, this juice is mixed with powder of the same nut. The compound is eaten with candied sugar, ghee of clarified, butter and honey.

Aphrodisin

A proprietary preparation compounded of the aphrodisiac yohimbine, together with aronacein, extract of miura puama and other ingredients. (Also see yohimbe)

Apples

Apples are a symbol of fertility that have always been associated with love, as they were sacred to Rhiannno, Celtic goddess of love and marriage as well as used in Viking and Greek love and fertility rituals. Also in Christian mythology, the apple was what Eve tempted Adam with in the Garden of Eden. In early British folk magic a woman can enslave the man of her choice by sleeping with an apple next to her skin and then persuading him to eat it. Whether making the fruit into dumpling, tart or turnover modified the magical effect is not recorded. In some ancient Scandinavian legends the apple is described as the 'food of the gods'. The belief was that the gods, grown old and decrepit, were rejuvenated by feasting on apples. There is possibly a reference here to cider, as the acids in apples are also mentioned.

Aquamarine

An engraved aquamarine was used among Arabs as a love charm to secure conjugal fidelity. Aquamarine has been used for relieving stress and soothing nerves since at least 2000 BCE in Egypt and the East. The Romans believed it was lucky for lovers maintaining youth, and health. Periapts, talismans, and various types of charms all play a prominent part, in both European and oriental erotology. As acknowledged amatory stimulants aquamarine is rules by Neptune.

Arabian Coffee

*(Coffea Arabica)*Arabian coffee has a reputation for its stimulating effect. Coffee was formerly a sacred beverage; African Sufis drank it for its invigorating effect when meditating. The stimulation that coffee produces also helps with sexual dysfunction.

Armagnac

King Henry 1V of France, before confronting his numerous mistresses, regularly fortified himself with a tiny glass of Armagnac. Wines and liqueurs have long been held to promote sexual activities.

Arris

A Hindu technique for dominating women sexually is to take pieces of arris root, mixed with mango oil, place them in a hole in the trunk of the sisu tree and left for six months. At the end of that time an ointment is prepared that will effectively be applied to the lingam, (male organ.) the women will then go wild with desire for that man.

Artichoke

(Cynara Scalyumus) A bristly plant, sometimes known to North American Indians as 'sun root' whose edible parts are the fleshy basis of the leaves; it was considered a powerful aphrodisiac, especially in France. Street vendors in Paris used to call;

Artichokes! Artichokes!
Heats the body and the spirit;
Heats the genitals

158

Catherine de Medici was fond of artichokes. Eating artichokes may directly produce euphoria; indirectly, this sense of pleasant relaxation encourages intercourse.

Asafoetida

(Ferula asa foetida/Ferula narthex) Asafoetida is a plant with turnip-like root. The root contains a milky sap that thickens on contact with air into resinous granules that smell like garlic, it grows in the valley of Kashmir in India and in Iran and Afghanistan. These granules are known as devil's dirt, or asafoetida, and are harvested in Asia and used in Ayurvedic and Tibetan medicine for their aphrodisiac value and for use in Asian cooking. It has also been found useful in the treatment of cases of habitual abortion.

Ashwagandha

(Withania somnifera) Ashwagandha is a small evergreen shrub of the nightshade family native to India, the Mediterranean and the Middle East. In Hindi or the Ancient Sanskrit language, the name means 'sweat of a horse' as those who take it are said to attain the strength and sexual vitality of a horse. It has been widely used in Ayurvedic medicine for thousands of years and one saying goes 'Ashwagandha enhances sex as surely as fire heats a pot.' Ashwagandha is classified as a rasayan, a rejuvenating or life extending agent; the rasayan are the most esteemed of Ayurvedic herbs. The Indian *Materia Mediaca* recommends the use of Ashwagandha for general debility, general aphrodisiac purposes, brain fatigue and low sperm count. Ashwagandha is a renowned aphrodisiac that improves sexual performance and is sometime used to treat impotence. It may be used for both men and women but its pro-sexual actions are probably best for the use in men.

Asoka

Asoka was named after the Hindu ruler of 299BCE who was a king of India. In Hindu sexology this plant, the lotus and jasmine provoke venery. The lotus itself is associated with the Lotus woman a Hindu Goddess, who was portrayed as standing on a lotus, she was the Indian Aphrodite and feminine ideal. (Also see Lotus)

Asparagus

(Asparagus officinalis/Asparagus racemosus) The asparagus plant is a climber with tiny white flowers that is cultivated all over the world but originates from India. The Egyptians, Greeks and Romans all valued asparagus as an aphrodisiac. It is ruled by Jupiter. The herbalist

159

Culpeper also wrote that "a decoction of asparagus roots could stirreth up bodily lust in man or woman." According to an Arab manual a daily dish of asparagus, boiled then fried in fat with egg yolks and a sprinkling of condiments will produce erotic effect. Its main use is as a galactogogue to increase milk secretion during lactation, it is also known to be useful for increasing the production of semen. It is best eaten with the fingers and dripping with butter, one drawback is the revolting odour that it gives to the urine afterwards. One old traditional saying goes: "A person who eats a lot of asparagus also has lots of lovers".

Ass
In Greek mythology the ass was the symbol of sexual potency. This animal was associated with satyrs and sileni, creatures who in their characteristic resembled satyrs. According to legend, at a Dionysian festival, Priapus personification of the sexual impulses, was about to consummate his sexual desire for the nymph Lotis. The braying of an ass however, interrupted the performance. Since then the ass became a sacrificial victim of Priapus. Pliny the Elder states that, "to increase sexual potency, the right testis of an ass should be worn in a bracelet". Such advice coincides with popular Oriental belief in the efficiency, for amatory purposes, of various types of charms and talismans made from animals reproductive parts i.e.; tiger and rhino sexual organs.

Aubergines
The aubergine, also known as 'eggplant' or, the 'apple of love', is regarded as an aphrodisiac in its native India. The *Kama Sutra* suggests rubbing a partner's body with aubergine juice to increase their libido. An aubergine split in half, a paste made of flour, water in which bois bandé has been boiled, together with pepper corns, chives, pimentos, and vanilla beans was a concoction used in the West Indies as a genital stimulant. The classic Turkish dish make from aubergine is imam bayildi, which means 'swooning imam'. It is said to make a man or woman swoon with desire.

Avocado *(Persea Americana)*
The avocado tree originates from Central America and was cultivated by the Mayan Indians. It was used as a medicine for women's complaints and as a nutritious food. The oil was also prized in ritual as an anointing agent. The seeds and the flesh are considered as aphrodisiac, and are said to lend vigour and kindle sexual interest.

The Aztecs called the avocado abuactl or testicle, a connection which seems to have impressed the Spanish conquistadores who exported the fruit back to Spain as a food and a sexual stimulant.

Ayahuasca *(Banisteriopsis caapi)*
The tree grows in tropical rain forests in the Amazon and is sacred to the Indians. It is also known as Ayahuasca, caapi, natema, and yagé. A psychedelic drug is made from the bark and shamans use it to go into healing trances. The drink is said to have an aphrodisiac effect and feelings of euphoria. It works by stimulating the hormones that maintain the erection.

Ba ji tian
(Morinda officialis) Ba ji tian is a deciduous plant native to China. Its roots yield a pungent, sweet tasting yellow dye. Ba ji tian is used to strengthen yang and is a popular pro-sexual tonic that strengthens the erection and can help to overcome impotence and premature ejaculation. It is also used to help treat male and female infertility and hormonal problems; such as irregular menstrual cycle in women.

Bamboo Shoots
Bamboo shoots are believed to produce an aphrodisiac reaction, and are popular in the orient, particularly in China were they are often used in oriental cuisine.

Bananas
(Musa acuminata Colla; Musa balbisiana Colla; Musa x paradisiaca L.) Bananas are one of the few foods with real potential as an aphrodisiac and not just for their phallic shape; the banana tree is actually an herb. Bananas contain an alkaloid (bufotenine) that acts on the brain to increase mood, self confidence and possibly increase sex

161

drive. It is found in greatest quality just beneath the skin, and is best obtained by cutting whole bananas lengthways and baking them with a little sugar or honey. The flesh should then be scraped away from the skin before eating. (Try baked bananas with walnuts and ice cream.)

Bangue

Bangue is mentioned by medieval writer Garcias as plants whose juice and leaves have aphrodisiac qualities. Bangue is probably a variant form of bhang.

Barbel

The fish, well prepared, helps to restore virility according to much ancient tradition.

Basil

(Ocimum sanchum, Ocimum basilicum) There are a number of varieties of basil, all of which originate from South Asia and are ruled by Mars God of War. The basil plant has a reputation as a strong aphrodisiac in Mexico and in Italy. Combine with pine nuts and garlic in Pesto sauce for a more tangy effect. Adding a mashed, grilled tomato softens the flavour and boosts its libidinous affect. In Italy basil symbolizes love and is often used by girls as a love charm. And according to an early 19th century physician, "basil helps the deficiency of Venus".

The tulasi plant *Ocimum sanctum* is one of the most holy plants of the Hindus. It is dedicated to the goddess Lakshmi and her husband Vishnu. The plant is said to provide abundant health and sexual vigour and is often planted in holy places and around altars.

According to magical practices of the Deep South and in voodoo, one should sprinkle basil on one's lover's food, or put basil in the bath to attract a new lover in to your life. Basil essential oil is very soothing if used for massage and an excellent addition to sensual blends of massage oils.

Bauba

In the ancient city of Miletus, an Ionian city in Asia Minor, there was a centre for the manufacture of aphrodisiacs, apparatus called olisboi or bauba in Greek.

Bay

(Laurus nobilis) Bay is ruled by the Sun and is also used in love magic. Take two needles, one for yourself and one to represent your lover or the one you desire. Lay the needles end to end so that the point of one is the eye of the other, and then wrap two bay leaves around them. Next

wind red thread around the packet, tightly and thoroughly so that it is completely covered. In Haiti it is said that whoever carries this packet in their gris gris bag can gain the love of any person they desire. Culpeper said: '...can procure women's courses; and speed deliver and expel the after birth'.

Beans
St Jerome forbade nuns to partake of beans, because they were often considered as an aphrodisiac food ruled by Venus. In Italy, broad bean soup is often taken as an assumed aphrodisiac. Beans in general have long been believed to possess amatory virtue. It gives a new meaning to 'full of beans'.

Beefsteak
Havelock Ellis, the renowned sexologist, regards the beefsteak as, "Probably as powerful a sexual stimulant as any other food".

Beer
In England, common belief attributes a beer to coital stimulus. Medical authority recommends that beer be taken along with food; although too much beer will have the opposite effect, i.e. 'brewers droop'.

Beets
White beets are attributed by Pliny the Elder, the Roman encyclopaedist, as helping to promote amorous ability. In general beets, carrots and turnips are all of aphrodisiac value and they are ruled by Jupiter.

Belladonna
(Altropa belladonna) Belladonna has shiny black fruits like cherries; Thessalian witches used belladonna to make love potions and it was often used in the Middle Ages as an inducement to a prospective sexual partner. Belladonna is a hazardous, poisonous drug extracted from the root and leaves of Deadly Nightshade. The name stems from the fact that Italian beauties made a cosmetic from the juice of the plant. The juice of the berry was used for the eyes, to brighten the eye and enlarge the pupils. In the Middle Ages belladonna formed an ingredient in the philtres and unguent prepared by witches, but it has no proven aphrodisiac value.

Benzoin
Benzoin is a standard ingredient in any incense of love. It seems to be especially potent when added to any incense used to call on the powers of Venus or Aphrodite.

Betal Palm

(Areca catechu) Native to the tropical forests of Asia the betel palm has small flowers and flamboyant orange/red fruits, the size of an egg, with hard seeds. The nut is crushed and the seeds chewed to stimulate the body sexually and counteract intestinal parasites; it often leaves a stain on the mouth and can lead to the loosening of teeth. The seeds, sometimes called 'ping lang' in China, and 'areca nut', 'pinang', 'siri suprari' in India have been used in Ayurvedic medicine and in religious ceremonies as an offering to the gods. The herb is ideal for posture meditation (asana) or when learning to control the body in the practice of yoga.

Betel pepper

(Piper betel) The betel pepper is a climbing vine with dark green leaves. It goes in the tropical area of Southeast Asia. It is often used in an erotic curry and is very stimulating. The Hindus call it 'morsels of desire'. There is some danger of over indulging in the betel morsels and this will have an anti-aphrodisiac effect.

Bhang

Bhang is a Sanskrit term meaning hemp. In India the leaves and seeds of hemp are chewed as a means of increasing sexual power. Frequently the seeds of hemp are mixed with musk, sugar and ambergris as an aphrodisiac medication.
(Also see hemp)

Bhuya-Kokali

(Solanum Jacquini) Bhuya-Kokali is a Hindu plant that is listed in the *Ananga-Ranga*, the erotic guide, as inducing aphrodisiac energy. The juice of the plant is dried in the sun and then mixed with honey, ghee or clarified butter and candied sugar.

Birds Nest Soup

Said to be an extremely aphrodisiac Chinese preparation. The nest of the sea sallow, made from edible sea weed stuck together by fish spawn, which abounds in phosphorus. The actual soup has no flavour until it is highly spiced. The Japanese had outdoor sex games and the

164

Chinese of the Ming period invented a game called 'bird finding nest' it took the form of a sexual drama played out in the open air.

Birdwort

A shrub used in medieval times and by the Romans as an aphrodisiac.

Bitter Sweet

An aromatic herb that was reputed to have aphrodisiac value.

Black Cohosh

(Cimicifuga racemosa) Black cohosh also known as 'squaw root' or 'black snakeroot' is an herbaceous perennial with creamy white flowers native to Canada and Eastern USA. The dried root of black cohosh is mainly used as a relaxant and a uterine stimulant, and hormonal balancer by American Indians.

Black Musali

(Curculigo orchiodes) A small perennial with an elongated tuberous root, stalk and lateral roots, Black Musali is grown wild in the Himalaya and India. It is an effective remedy for problems of the reproductive system. Legends of ancient times state that it is an herb that endows and individual with a great deal of strength and also has effective aphrodisiac qualities. It is indicated in erectile impotence, spermatorrhoea and menorrhagia.

Black Pepper

(Piper Nigrum Linn) Pungent black pepper has a reputation for bringing spice to the bedroom as well as the palate. Pepper was so precious in ancient times that it was used as money to pay taxes, tributes, dowries, and rent. It was weighed like gold and used as a common medium of exchange. In A.D. 410, when Rome was captured, 3,000 pounds of pepper were demanded as ransom.

Body

Believers in astrology can please, surprise and delight their lovers by kissing, caressing and even massaging the parts of the body associated with an individual's sun sign. (See chart in appendix 3)

Bois Bandé

Tightening wood, a concoction administered in the West Indies by women, it has the reputed virtue of an aphrodisiac. The ingredients contain the bark of a tree which itself contains bucine and a little strychnine; the preparation is poison. Bois Bande loosely translates from its French origin as 'Potency Wood'. The bark of the Bois Bandé tree is sometimes soaked in rum and drunk for sexual problems

165

Borax

According to 17th century belief, refined borax excites powerful desire. Nicholas Venette, a Frenchman, recommends it as a substance that readily pervades all parts of the body.

Blood

Human blood has been thought to be anti aphrodisiac and has been often used for this purpose. Faustina, the wife of the emperor Antoninus Pius, fell in love with a gladiator. The magicians whom the Emperor consulted advised that she drink her lover's blood, the effect being that she would conceive a permanent hatred for the gladiator. In 17th century Hungary, Countess Elizabeth Bathory was notorious in attempting to achieve rejuvenation by bathing in the blood of eighty strangled virgins. She was caught and condemned to life imprisonment. Vampires' blood drinking is found to be very sexual and much modern fiction has played on the erotic foreplay and seduction of the vampire society, even today there are vampire cults that indulge in ritual blood drinking.

Bones

Camel bone as an aphrodisiac aid. Indian erotology suggest that camel bone is dipped in the juice of the eclipta prestata plant; then burnt. The black pigment produced from the ashes is placed in a box also made of camel bone and then applied with antimony to the eyelashes with the pencil of a camel bone. The effect, it is hinted, will be erotic sub-jugations. A Hindu erotic text suggests the stimulating and alluring effect of bone of peacock or hyena, covered with gold and tied to the right hand will induce sexual strength and power. (Also see rhino horn)

Borrachero

(Methysticodendron amesianum) Borrachero is a tree that grows in Columbia, the name means drunkard, and it has white funnel shaped flowers that hang down. These exude a scent much like that of Dataura. The Indians plant the tree for its beauty, and use its leaves for their medical, psychedelic and aphrodisiac effects. The effects are similar to those of angel's trumpet; but Borrachero has a stronger end product.

Brains

The brain of calf, sheep and pig, young and served fresh, are reputedly erotic in their effects. As a side dish in Mediterranean counties, brains are a special delicacy when properly prepared. The medieval philosopher and occultist Albertus Magnus stated in his writings that brain could be used in formulas for love potions. He particularly recommended the brains of a partridge ground into a powder and swallowed in red wine.

Brasica Eruca

Brasica eruca was sown in the garden of a monastery and was taken as a daily infusion by monks, in medieval times, under the impression that it would cheer and rouse them, from customary sluggishness. But the continued use of it produced such a strong aphrodisiac effect that the coenobites transgressed alike their monastery walls and vows.

Brunfelsia

(Brunfelsia species) Brunfelsia grows in the Amazon rainforest. It has five leaved flower of a violet colour. The root is the source of the manaca root, a remedy for snake bites. Many Indians use it as an aphrodisiac.

Bull's testicles

Bull's testicles is a renowned Spanish dish that is said to increase the libido. There is no proof to this claim.

Brya

(Fabaceae) Brya also known as 'ebony coccuswood'. According to Pliny the Elder, the Roman encyclopaedist, "the ashes of the plant called in Latin Brya, mixed with the urine of ox, produced impotence".

Bufotenin

A dangerous drug that is chemically related to mescaline; the drug is obtained from the skin of a poisonous tropical toad. The substance bufotoxin is the chief extract of the toad's venom. This alkaloid is also present in the seeds of a mimosa plant that is related to the *leguminosae* family. The natives of some South American tribes use this drug as an aphrodisiac in the form of a snuff called cohaba. Bufotenin is capable of producing severe hallucinations of a psycho-erotic nature. Its use is highly dangerous and in any case requires the supervision and control of a physician or psychiatrist.

Burdock Root

(Arctium lappa, A. minus) Burdock root can be used in a tea as a tonic to the liver and blood. The fresh root is also delicious stir fried and is very stimulating to the circulation generally; considered by many to be an aphrodisiac.

Burgundy
In moderation, considered a wholesome aphrodisiac, this is in line with belief in the amatory effects produced by many wines and liqueurs if taken in moderation.
Buttermilk bath
An anti-aphrodisiac, suggested in Hindu erotological literature as a way for women to negate amatory challenges, is to bathe in the buttermilk of a buffalo. The milk is to be mixed with powders of the golpalika plant, the banupadika plant, and yellow amaranth.

Cabbage
Cabbage is ruled the Moon and used in many traditional aphrodisiac preparations, wild cabbage is frequently an ingredient in lust inducing spells.
Cacao Tree
(Theobroma cacao) The evergreen cacao tree grows in the Caribbean and in Central America. According to an ancient Indian recipe; roasted cocoa beans are ground and dissolved in water along with other ingredients, vanilla, cayenne, pepper, matico pepper, pimento, canella squash seeds and a cup of gold. The resulting beverage which was originally known as chocolati (chocolate) can then be consumed. In ancient America cocoa was considered a 'food of the gods' and was a popular aphrodisiac. Aztec prostitutes were paid in cocoa. Eating chocolate can increase brain levels of several chemicals including mood altering PEA *(phenyl ethylamine)* which produce a mild, confidence instilling buzz. Chocolate also contains tryptophan, a chemical converted to serotonin in the body and therobromine, which peps you up, three reasons why chocolate is so addictive. The fourth reason is that chocolate uniquely melts in the mouth at body temperature, and is

very sensual to eat. Yet belief in the aphrodisiac value of chocolate prevailed for a long time. In the 17th century monks in France were forbidden to drink chocolate on account of its reputed aphrodisiac properties. Chocolate is sacred to the fierce love goddess of the Aztecs; it was regarded as a rare and powerful aphrodisiac in 17th century Europe. The Sun King Louis XIV anticipated modern advertising by luring women to his bed with gifts of chocolates. In 18th century France, many aphrodisiac dishes and pastries were compounded with chocolate. Cocoa has been held to be an aphrodisiac. (Also see chapter 10 on chocolate)

Cajueiro

(Anacardium occidentale) Cajueiro, also known as 'cashew nut', is an evergreen tree related to poison ivy and the mango, native to tropical America. The fruit of the Cajueiro has a sweet flavour and is considered an aphrodisiac in Brazil. It is used together with Catuaba and Muira puma to treat impotence, the bark is also used to make a treatment for vaginal discharge and is said to be a contraceptive.

Cakes

In the Middle Ages, spiced cakes were often baked in a small oven over the naked body of a woman who wanted to retain the affections of her lover. The witch who carried out the baking technique used this form of sympathetic magic to arouse desires in correspondence with the flaming heat of the oven. The baked creation would ultimately be offered to the object of the woman's love. Such cakes were sometime consumed by parties, the man and the woman, as a means of strengthening and cementing passion. The practise was common though-out Europe and similar ceremonies are not unknown in other countries as well.

Calamint or Mountain mint

(Calamintha officinalis) Calamint, Ruler Mercury, belongs to a genus closely related to both the Thymes and to Catnep and Ground Ivy. Calamint is an aromatic herb that was in the past used in India for erotic practices. Gerard says, "The seede cureth the infirmities of the heart, taketh away sorrowfulnesse which commeth of melancholie, and maketh a man merrie and glad."

Calamus

(Acorus Calamus) This plant grows in the Southern Asian marshlands and North American plains. It has been used in medicine baths, teas and

169

incenses in many areas. The North American Indians chew the root to ward off exhaustion and it is said to have a rejuvenating effect on the sexual life, best used in herbal baths to awaken sexual desire.

Camel

Various parts of the camel have been used in aphrodisiac preparations; the fat of the camels hump melted down is suggested in an Oriental manual as an aphrodisiac aid. Its bones burnt, and its milk with honey will improve potency according to Arab traditions.

Camphor

(Cinnamomum camphora) Camphor is a concrete volatile oil obtained by distillation with water and the wood of the tree. A form of camphor known as mono-bromated camphor is said to have an aphrodisiac effect. Its great value is in colds, chills, and in all inflammatory complaints; it relieves irritation of the sexual organs.

Cardamom Pod

(Elettaria cardamonmum) Cardamom tea is said to have distinct aphrodisiac properties, and makes a good bedtime tea.

Carnation

Magically the flowers can be used in any rites of love and seduction. The petals are dried and scattered in pot pourri, or given in sachets, to engaged couples to keep their love life fresh and joyful. But do be sure that you use any colour except white carnation flowers as these are used in spells to cool ardour and can be made into an an-aphrodisiac potion. In incense or perfumes, carnation is used to increase personal magnetism and boost self assurance and can be used in rituals of healing and in aphrodisiacs.

Cannabis Indica

(Cannabis sataiva) Indian hemp is a drug that was used for centuries as an aphrodisiac. The plant grows in Central and Western Asia and can be grown in many other parts of the world inducing North America and Europe when the right conditions are supplied. One of the oldest archaeological relics in existence is a fragment of hemp cloth found at Catal Huyuk that dates back to 8000 BCE. The plant is also mentioned as an aphrodisiac in Assyrian texts, where it is called qu-nu-bu. In Istanbul hemp seeds were customarily roasted and salted and served at wedding dinners and during medieval times cannabis was taken as a ceremonial drink in the temples of India to reach religious ecstasy. The use of cannabis can prolong and intensify the sexual experience, but

prolonged use dulls the senses and can be an-aphrodisiac for some men. The resin extracted from the plant is called cannabinon, from which cannabinol stems, a red oily substance found in the flowering tops of the female plant. Extracted from the plant in pure form, it is known in India as Charas.

Another weaker form is known as Bhang, which is used as a beverage, In Mexico, it is known as Marihuana, and another form is ganja, made from the cut crop of the female plant. It is used for smoking.

In the 7th century A.D. the Assyrians began to use the drug for is narcotic powers, in the 2nd century B.C. the ancient Chinese physician Hua Tu administered a narcotic draught to his patients before an operation. the drug was known as Ma Fu Shuan.

It was used by Dioscorides, the Greek army physician in the 1st century A.D. to relieve pain. *The Arabian Nights* are filled with allusions to hashish, King Omar castes the Princess Alrizah into a deep sleep with some concentrated bhang. Again, the thief, Armad Kanakim, drugs the guards with hemp fumes.

Cantharides

(Mylabris, lytta vesicatoria) Cantharides is a species of beetle found in Southern Europe, was first mentioned by Aristotle: the active principle is a white powder called cantharidine. Cantharides if used externally may have fatal results, taken internally the drug causes death. It was widely used in the 18th century as a sexual stimulant, cooked in biscuits, cakes a pastry and inserted in candies and chocolates.

An 18th century French play refers to the drug and it was known to Dioscorides an army physician in the 1st century, who produced a Materia medical, Galen, a Greek physician of the 2nd century A.D. and the Arab philosopher and physician Avicenna. It is also recorded that Madame de Pompadour used a tincture of cantharides to regain the love of Louis XV.

Caperberry

(Capparis spinosa) Anciently, the berry of the caper plant was considered a strong aphrodisiac. In the bible, the term is used synonymously with sexual desire. Caperberry in Hebrew means, 'provocative of desire'. This is a reference to its use as an aphrodisiac. Immature fruit of the caper berry is taken from the plant for its uses. It grows in clefts of rocks and walls. Ecclesiastes 12:5 says the caper will be ineffective and that 'desire shall fade'. This refers to the loss of

171

intensity of the senses in advanced age. Caper was taken as a stimulant to these senses.

Caraway

(Carum carvi) Caraway has a reputed aphrodisiac virtue; it is frequently mentioned in Oriental sex manuals and love or passion inducing recipes. Several liqueurs are made with caraway, including Kummel and some Schnapps.

Cardamom

(Elettaria cardamonmum) Cardamom is an herbaceous plant found in the rain forest of Southeast Asia. When touched the entire plant exudes a pleasant cinnamon scent. Grind 1/3 cup each of white sesame seeds and flaxseeds, then add 1 tablespoon cardamom and 2 tablespoons sucanat (unrefined sugar). This can be sprinkled on yogurt and cereal. It is used to flavour food, especially rice, teas and beverages; and has been known as an  aphrodisiac since ancient time. Favourite dishes include rice pudding with rose water and chopped dates or sprinkle on fruit salad with toasted nuts. A pounded mixture of cardamom spice seeds, ginger and cinnamon, sprinkled over boiled onions and green peas, is considered in Arab countries, as an effective dish for promoting sexual vitality.

Cardoon

(Cardunculus) Prickly plants, akin to artichoke, the fleshy parts of the inner leaves are eaten as an aphrodisiac, principally in France.

Carrot

(Daucus carota) Carrot, ruler Mercury, the ancient Greeks believed that all parts of the carrot were aphrodisiac and ate the seeds, root and foliage when preparing for an orgy. They were known as 'philon', meaning loving, and were often given to potential sex partners to stimulate their passion. Among Arabs, carrots are eaten as an aphrodisiac, stewed in milk sauce, they are recommended to help sexual activity. Eaten raw or cooked they have diuretic and invigorating qualities.

Castor Oil

(Ricinus communis) The Castor Oil plant is a native of India, where it bears several ancient Sanskrit names, the most ancient and most usual being 'Eranda', which has passed into several other Indian languages. Caster oil was once popular among American Indians for erotic purposes; it was used as a base for mixing various herbs to prolong intercourse.

Catancy

Catancy is a plant that the witches of ancient Thessaly, in Greece used in love philtres.

Catuaba

(Erythroxylon catuaba; Juniperus brasiliensis; Amemopaegma mirandum) Catuaba is often know as the 'tree of togetherness' or the 'tree of love' by the Tupi Indians in Brazil and is one of the most successful pro-sexual herbs available. There are two species of catuaba that grow in Brazil and small yellow flowers and dark yellow fruits. In Brazil it is called a tonic for the genitals. The Tupi Indians first discovered the pro-sexual action of catuaba. There is a famous Brazilian saying, "Until a father reaches 60, the son is his; after that the son is from catuaba". The supplement is widely used to treat impotence and as an aid for fertility in older males. Catuaba tree bark contains aromatic resins and non-addictive alkaloids, catuabins, which are distantly related to cocaine. It acts as a sexual stimulant and natural aphrodisiac, promoting erotic dreams and increased sexual energy in men and women. Catuaba has been used in trials to help HIV and AIDS as part of treatment plans to improve quality of life among the infected.

Caviar

Caviar is in general considered to be a stimulant to sensual inclinations; it is invariable present at dinners and banquets that stress rich, erotic dishes accompanied by appropriate wines, resulting for the diners, in a sense of widespread euphoria. Such a condition is highly conducive to amatory exercises, as French and other European fiction illustrates so lavishly. The salty, musky aroma and pungent flavour of caviar is a renowned aphrodisiac that is said to remind lusty males of the female genitals. Caviar possibly will contain steroidal compounds that might boost sex drive but probably only in quantities that few today could afford.

Cayenne

(Capsicum frutescens) Cayenne, or chilli pepper, is a perennial shrub native to Mexico and Central America, but is now found through the tropics. Cayenne is widely known as a hot spicy supplement that stimulates circulation to the hands, feet and genitals, and promotes sweating. It is sometimes used as a snuff and said to have aphrodisiac properties and helps to maintain an erection.

Cedar

The tree is particularly sacred to the god Tammuz the Assyrian vegetation god. Sacrificed each year by the goddess Ishtar, he thus alternates as god of the growing year, and king of the underworld where his consort is Ishtar's dark sister Erishkagal. The oil and wood can be used in any incense or perfume dedicated to the horned one. As it is also a reputed aphrodisiac it has very vigorous sexual properties and can be added to any seduction incenses or pouches.

Celery

(Apium graveolens) Celery like the truffle is said to contain an aphrodisiac substance similar to a pig pheromone which also has a pro-sexual action in humans. In 18th century France, celery soup was a means of whetting the amorous appetite, it was often included in love recipes. Celery cream was a concoction that is said to exercise urgency of the vita sexualis. Used in soups as well as raw; considered an excellent way to strengthen all the organs of the body.

Chaldean Device

In ancient Chaldean culture, religion and health were in intricately linked to each other, and the use of magical charms, like the chaldean device, were used and invocations were made to powerful gods. In the case of love magic it was a belief, fostered by the traditions of Chaldean priests, that vigour and sexual activity could be restored or increased by eating the marrow or the liver of young boys. The belief is widespread with those of certain primitive tribes that, both in the African continent and the Pacific islands, have sought supreme courage by eating the heart and brain of a vanquished enemy.

Chameleon Milk

Milk of chameleon was recommended as an erotic stimulant by Avicenna. Avicenna was a famous 13th century Arab philosopher and physician. His Arab name is Abu Ali al-Hussain ibn Sina. A noted libertine as well, he discussed in his writing erotic questions, sex procedures and aphrodisiacs.

174

Champagne
Long associated with erotic situations, amatory relationships and intimate dining. In general, wines have, throughout history, traditionally been of significant aid in amatory ventures. Champagne particularly excites the senses and is known as the wine of the bedroom; the feminine forms of champagne can even be made to blush.

Charms
The cestus was girdle of Venus that had the power of exciting love. In Homer's Iliad, this girdle is 'the charm of love and desire that subdues all the hearts of immortal gods and mortal men.' Gabriel Clauder, author of a dissertation, *De Philris*, Published in 1661 discusses, historically and medically, the uses of charms, philtres and potions of all kinds. Some were concocted for poisoning purposes others as love charms. Among some of the ingredients mentioned by Clauder are laurel and olive leaves, milk and saliva. Among ancient and Oriental races love charms were often associated with the technique known as sympathetic magic. A charm was uttered over betel nuts, the nuts were then place in a box, and the person who opened the box fell in passionate love with the owner. Or a charm was uttered over the oil used by a woman or over a lock of her hair. The hoped-for result was similar to aphrodisiac stimulants. The ancients, among them the Greeks, felt that the human liver was the seat of all desires; hence it became a love fetish and an aphrodisiac symbol. Among one of the strangest of charms is the udder of the Hyena, tied on the left arm, which enticed the affection of any desired woman.

Chartreuse
Said to be an irresistible sexual excitant for women. In its green form chartreuse was popular in the 19th century.

Chaste Tree Berry
(Vitrex agnus castus) Agnus castus also known as the chaste tree, is a deciduous, aromatic tree with palm shaped laves and small lilac flowers. It is native to the Mediterranean and West Asia and was traditionally used by monks to reduce sex drive and was often called 'monks pepper tree'. Chaste tree also has the reputation of boosting sex drive, hormonal problems and fertility in women. I would recommend this supplement for women with hormonal problems or during menopause.

175

Cheese

Cheese was highly esteemed for its aphrodisiac property, parmesan cheese in particularity in 18th century France, was considered highly beneficial in this way.

Cherries

(Prunus serotina) Cherries, ruler Venus, were considered stimulation and often included in love cookery. Cherry bark has been used in magic to make your lover more passionate; wrap your lovers' picture in red cloth along with the cherry bark to keep them keen.

Chestnuts

(Fagaceae family, genus Castanea.) Ruled by Jupiter Chestnuts, soaked in muscadel, then oiled, along with Satyrion, pistachio nuts, pine kernel, chubels, cinnamon, rocket seed and sugar, compounded together, these ingredients form an invigorating electuary. This compound was popular as an old English love recipe. Culpeper said that chestnuts affected the blood; this could help with maintaining an erection.

Earth chestnuts

(Bulbes de cerfeuil, or bunium bulbocastonum) Sometimes called earth nuts, ground nuts, ciper nuts and in Sussex pig nuts: ruled by Venus. They are said by Culpeper to provoke lust, and are also good for the urinary system in general provoking urination and clearing the membranes of the penis allowing erection.

Chick Peas

(Cicer arietinum) You can take juice of powdered onions and purified honey, heated until the onion juice disappears, the residue is then cooled and mixed with water and pounded chick peas. Taken before bedtime in winter, the beverage is described in an Arab manual as particularly stimulating for sexual prowess.

Chicory

(Cichorium intybus) Asteraceae) Chicory was commonly included in medieval love potions and was given to lovers to encourage faithfulness.

Chillies

Chillies can also be added to food to arouse the interest of a reluctant lover, containing high levels of vitamins A and C, along with vitamins E and B1-3. They are very powerful and too much will have the opposite effect not surprisingly therefore chillies can be added to a sachet of food to banish an unwanted lover.

Chilito

(Epithelantha micromeres) Chilito is a round thorny cactus that grows in Mexico; and has red pepper like fruits. The flesh or the fruit resembles chilli pepper, thus the Mexican name Chilito or 'little chile'. The Tarahumara Indians eat the fruit as a stimulant as an aphrodisiac; it is also reputed to repel evil forces. The cactus is one of the so called 'false peyote's', which Indian magicians use as a substitute for the genuine peyote.

Chocolate

(Theobroma cacao) (See cacao tree and chapter 10 on chocolate) Chocolate was sacred to the fierce love goddess of the Aztecs, and regarded as a powerful aphrodisiac in 17th century Europe. The Sun King, Louis XIV, anticipated modern advertising by luring women to his bed with gifts of chocolates.

Chuchahuasi

(Maytenus krukovit; M. ebenfolia; M. macrocarpa) Chuchuhuasi is prepared from the root bark of a large tree, when steeped in white rum for a week and mixed with honey it is taken as one of the best known jungle aphrodisiacs in Columbia and Peru. Chuchuhuasi is reputed to enhance virility, prolong an erection and to cure male impotence.

Chutney

A relish compounded of herbs, fruits, and various seasonings commonly used in the Orient for its reputation for stimulating the libido.

Cider

Cider has been credited as an aphrodisiac and has often been mentioned in fiction as an amatory aid. (See apples)

Cinchona

A Peruvian bark that is used as a tonic, it has frequently been credited with the property of stimulating erotic expressions and maintaining an erect penis.

Cinnamon

(Cinnamomum zeylanicum, cinnamomum cassia) Cinnamon is the dried inner bark of an East India tree used as a spice with reputed erotic effect. Many centuries ago a cinnamon liqueur was famous as an aphrodisiac at the courts of the Indian Maharajas. The evergreen cinnamon grows in Southeast Asia. The young leaves are often bright red; in contrast the flowers and fruits are small and inconspicuous.

The bark is peeled and dried; used in cooking as a spicy flavouring, or made into an oil. The oil is used in the perfume industry and has a reputation as an aphrodisiac since ancient times. It has been used as an oil rubbed on the genitals for erotic stimulation. (Don't try this!)

Civet

The civet cat produced a musk that was widely used in perfume, the French royal court used to offer sweets perfumed with civet to desirable ladies. Civet cats were also bred for their secretions that formed the base of perfumes and were also of aphrodisiac value. It is of interest to note that Daniel Defoe, author of *Robinson Crusoe*, was for a time the owner of a civet cat farm.

Clary

(Salvia sclarea) Clary, ruler Moon, is closely related to genuine sage (*salvia officinalis*) also known as muscatel sage. The plant has been used since ancient times as a spice and medicine. It was mentioned by Dioscorides as having the ability to kindle sexual desire. Culpeper said that the seeds taken in wine provoked venery.

Wild Clary

Ruler the Moon. The seeds being beaten to powder and drank with wine are said to provoke lust.

Clams

Clams are reputed to possess marked aphrodisiac properties as are many kinds of sea foods. In mythology the clam represents the womb and female sexuality.

Cloves

(Eugenia caryophyllata) The clove tree grows in tropical areas and has leathery leaves and tiny flowers and long fruits. The clove has been used as an aphrodisiac for 5,000 years but overdoses of the plant can have very unpleasant side effect. Cloves are associated with the powers of the Sun and Jupiter and are sacred to Cemunnos, the horned god. They are a potent fertility symbol because they look very like a miniature penis. They are therefore extremely useful in many rites of lust and seduction and can be used ether in incense, philtres or perfumes. Pounded cloves in a little milk were recommended by an Italian erotologist. A little of the essential oil added to any seduction oil encourages the opposite sex to desire physical contact and is an aphrodisiac. According to a magical Persian recipe:

Cloves, cinnamon, and cardamoms are put in a jar and cover them, then read backwards a chapter of the Koran, Then fill the jar with rose water and steep a husband's shirt in it with a piece of parchment inscribed with his name and the name of four angels. Heat together over a fire, when the mixture boils the husband's love will increase.

Coca shrub

(Erythroxylum coca) The coca shrub in indigenous to the South American Andes and has been cultivated for over 3,000 years. In ancient Indian cultures the coca shrub was considered a gift from the gods and viewed as sacred. Its leaves were used for oracular, medicinal and religious purposes. The fresh leaves have long been chewed and made into a tea as a stimulant, and as an aphrodisiac. The coca shrub was also sacred to the Inca, who considered it a gift of the gods. The shrub was the home of Mama Coca, a seductive, wonderful woman who could bless her devotees with her powers.

Strict rules governed the use of coca leaves; they were offered to the gods, chewed in their honour, burned or smoked. They were given to the populace during religious and state festivals as an aphrodisiac in religious and ritual act. To ensure that Mama Coca was in a favourable mood, the collector was required to have slept with a woman before he went out to the coca harvest, and the leaves were then picked in her name.

The original coca cola contained extract of coca leaves and cola nuts; it was very stimulating, sold as a medicinal tonic and certainly an outstanding aphrodisiac. The success of the original beverage has not abated, even thought the modern version contains neither cocaine nor the stimulating juice of the cola nut.

In 1859 Sigmund Freud published his experiences with coca leaves and cocaine in the *Centralblatt für die gesamte Therapie*. He also discussed its aphrodisiac effects: 'Coca is an aphrodisiac, the natives of South America, who portray their Goddess of Love with coca leaves in her hand, had no doubt about the arousing effect of coca on the genital domain....'

With Freud's publication, cocaine became famous overnight. It very quickly became fashionable in circles fond of good living, since its effect upon sexuality are so pronounced its mere use became a disreputable erotic adventure, for many, however what began as a stimulating recreational diversion became a fatal addiction.

All parts of the plant but especially the fresh leafs contain cocaine, the main active ingredient. This substance has a stimulating effect on the central nervous system heightening the sensibilities. Coca has known effects upon the sphincter; it relieves pain, relaxes and makes it more receptive to pleasure. Thus cocaine is a drug much favoured by homosexuals.

Cocaine

Today cocaine is known as the magical white powder of the rich and super rich, it has conquered the world. It is sniffed at work, at parties and as an aphrodisiac. Cocaine is correctly considered as an erotic drug or an aphrodisiac. A man who ingests cocaine can maintain the erection of his penis even after one or two orgasms and it makes possible the greater control over orgasm. But cocaine is a very dangerous habit forming drug, whose use provokes sexual desire and excitement in both sexes, but particularly in women. If used long term it can lead to sexual perversions, immorality and break down in all moral restraint.

Cockles

Cockles are considered to have stimulatory aphrodisiac properties. Many kind of sea food have traditionally been so considered. The Greek encyclopaedist, Athenaeus, author of *The Banquet of the Philosophers*, mentions the efficiency of seafoods as aphrodisiacs.

Coco-de-Mer

(Lodoicea maldivica) The coco-de-mer or double coconut occurs wild only in the Seychelles. The palm is dioecious with the female plant forming enormous fruits that resemble the female pelvis. The resemblance is so vivid that rumour has it that the temple of Venus was carved in to the wood. The natives believe that the palms unite as man and woman during stormy nights. Despite this the coco-de-mer has no proven aphrodisiac properties.

Coconut Palm

(Cocos nucifera) Today the coconut palm grows all over the temperate world and is often cultivated in plantations and gardens. All parts of the plant can be utilized; the roots are made into traditional remedies, the flower stem is tapped to obtain palm wine, the nut is eaten and used for its oil. Palm wine is said to be aphrodisiac, and the coconut milk mixed with thorn apple seeds and honey is a great tonic. Palm wine can also be distilled into powerful schnapps known as arak.

Cod liver oil and cod roe
These are both considered to have aphrodisiacal properties.
Coffee
(Caffea) Coffee is said to dull the sexual urge, a 17th century traveller in Persia describes the Khan as smoking narghileh, in addition, the Khan drinks a kind of black liquid called Kahowa, (coffee) that seems to subdue the senses and deter lasciviousness.
Cognac
The drink Cognac with the addition of a little paprika and the yolk of an egg was often considered an efficient aphrodisiac.
Cola
(Cola nitida) Known today as a refreshing drink, but also known as bichy, it is obtained from the dried seeds of a plant called cola nitida. The seeds or nuts are common in Africa, have a star shaped husked capsule, where they are used as currency and often as charms and sacred objects. Cola is chewed by the natives, and is believed to endow them with vigour; it is also reputedly a sexual stimulant; it was often used in love magic. The drink we know today as cola or coca cola was first made from a distilled process of the coca leaf, now used to make cocaine.
Colewort
(Brassica oleracea acephala) Among the Romans, this herb was associated with lascivious activities and was dedicated to the phallic god Priapus.
Collyruim
Collyruim is a Latin term meaning eye-salve. These salves were used by the Romans and the Hindu and were reputed to have a stimulating effect on sexual relationships. In addition collyrium was endowed with traditional magical properties as a love charm.
Conitech Cowlage
(Atmagupta Macuna pruriens) A slender climbing annual which grows in the foothills of the Himalayas and in the plains of India and Sri Lanka, Conitech works on the reproductive system and is used to promote male virility.
Coral Tree
(Erthrina Americana) The coral tree has beanlike leaves, red racemes and pod like fruit with bright red seeds. It has a reputation for making the local women easy and willing to have sex with any available man.

181

The beans are also made in to necklace and worn as a sign of consent.

Coriander

(Coriandrum sativum) This annual herb was introduced by the Romans, who adapted its use from the Greeks. This in turn was learnt from the Egyptians and their African neighbours. Coriander seed are mentioned in the tales of the Arabian Nights and are still prized by Arabs as a famous aphrodisiac. To the ancient Chinese, coriander seed was believed to confer immortality and have magical regenerative powers. This is probably linked to its powers as a love potion, as when the old herbals talk of herbs as a 'rejuvenator' to make one young again, they do not mean the smoothing of wrinkles and the restoring of youth, and they refer to restoration or youthful sexual vigour. Albertus Magnus, the 13th century philosopher and occultist, said that coriander, valerian and violet are love inducing herbs, they should, however, be gathered in the last quarter of the moon. In magic, coriander is used in love philtres, especially those concerned with physical sexuality. Anglo Saxons used coriander seed in spells to ease childbirth. It is also recorded that Arab women chew the seeds to relieve some of the pains of childbirth.

Cotton

(Cossypium herbaceum) The root of the cotton plant has been used in remedies and the seeds contain a valuable oil. In China the roots of the cotton plant were used to inhibit the production of semen. In the Ayurvedic system the root cortex of the cotton plant is considered a tonic and rejuvenator.

Country Mallow

(Bala Sida cordifolia) Country mallow is a plant with strong roots and sturdy stature grown as an herb in India. It has been found useful for problems with the reproductive system, used in Ayurvedic medicine for sexual disjunction problems for impotence, seminal and other debilities such as for increasing sperm count.

Cow wheat

(Melampryum pratense) Cow wheat is a tall plant with yellow flowers, used to feed cows. But Pliny the Elder the Roman encyclopaedist and Dioscorides the physician say that it inflames desire and amatory passions.

Crab Apples

(Malus sylvestris) Crab apples are often made into jellies and jams and are reputed to have a stimulating effect on one's sex drive.

182

Crabs
As with most other shell fish crabs are reputed to be aphrodisiac. The Greeks highly prized dressed crab in feasts of love and seduction.

Crayfish
Crayfish was particularly favoured in the Mediterranean and considered of high aphrodisiac potency. There is a tradition in the deep south of North America particularly in New Orleans "If you want to make your partner hot for sex, feed them some crayfish in gumbo and the night is yours".

Cress
(Apium nodiflorum) Cress, ruler Saturn, is most often used in salads and as a dressing for food. It is said to be aphrodisiac if eaten raw or boiled, or drunk as a juice. The plant was cultivated in Italy and the East for its sexual value. Ovid, Martial, and Columella, all Roman poets, testify to its erotic power. Hence it was called *impudica,* (shameless). Marcellus Empiricus a Roman physician, prescribed three scruples of cress, three of red onion, three of pine seed, three of Indian nard for impotence. Apicius, author of a Roman cookbook, recommends for the consummation of desire, onions cooked in water with pine seeds and cress juice seasoned with pepper.

Crocodile
Crocodile teeth, states Pliny he Elder, in his *Historia Naturalis*, attached to the right arm, will act as an aphrodisiac. Crocodile tail is also a sexual delicacy, the Roman poet Horace said that the excrement of the crocodile has aphrodisiac virtues; I am not sure what one was meant to do with it!

Cubeb
(Piper cubeba, fam Piperaceae) The cubeb which is indigenous to Java is a berry similar to a grain of pepper, with a very pungent flavour. It is used in cookery and in medicine. A drink made from cubeb pepper is described as a strong aphrodisiac in many Arabic manuals. Chewing cubeb pepper also produces similar results, so does powdered cubeb mixed with honey and or wine. In China an infusion of cubeb pepper leaves is prepared as a highly stimulating aphrodisiac. Eating cubebs as a sexual stimulant was suggested by the 13th century Arab philosopher and physician Avicenna. In voodoo magic cubeb berries are known as 'love berries'. Use them in or bath water or carry in a red flannel bag to be ready for love.

Cucumbers
(Cucurbitaceae) Ruler the Moon. Cucumber probably gains its reputation as an aphrodisiac due to its suggestive length, circumference and resemblance to the male member, this is not proven; but it is good for the urinary system.

Cumin
(Cumin Cyuminum) Cumin is an aromatic plant, similar to fennel, used as a condiment and alleged to have an erotic stimulator effect and be an aphrodisiac.

Cup of gold
(Solandra brevicalyx) Cup of gold is a climbing plant that grows in the Americas. It has long yellow funnel shaped flowers. The Indians of Mexico have cultivated cup of gold as an ornamental, magical and medicinal plant. The females of the Lacandon Maya used the flowers to perfume their clothes and attract men. Other members of the tribe used them to make an aphrodisiac drink. The root makes a psychedelic drink that also has aphrodisiac effect. The Aztec mixed the leaves with cocoa to blend an erotic love drink.

Curry
Curry, now Britain's favourite take-away, was originally an oriental dish flavoured with spices, and reputedly a sexual stimulant, because it heated the blood.

Cuttle-fish
Cuttle-fish, spiced oyster, sea hedge-hogs and lobster were among the ingredients of love potions that the reputed thaumaturgish Apuleius, 2nd century A.D. was accused of having prepared to win the love of a widow according to the De Magia.

Cyclamen
(Primulaceae) The root of the cyclamen, snowbread, was used in ancient times as one of the ingredients in love potions.

Damiana or Saint Damian

(Turnera diffusa aphrodisiac) Ruler Venus, a small shrub with aromatic leaves, native of Central America, Mexico, Namibia and the Caribbean. It can be smoked and brewed as a tea and used as a potent alcohol. Its volatile, aromatic oils and beta sitosterol have a stimulatory effect on the sexual organs and a gentle irritant effect on the urogenital tract to produce a local stimulant effect with tingling and throbbing sensations. Its alkaloids may also boost circulation to the genital area and increase sensitivity of nerve endings in the clitoris and penis. It also increases circulation to the penis so that erections are firmer and last longer, thus increasing sexual desire. It is a powerful aphrodisiac and is very potent and vigorous in love rites, particularly helpful to one seeking a magical partner or a person to share your life, magical studies and practise. It is known to voodoo practitioners where it is used in love spells or to bring back a straying lover.

Damiana is one of the very few substances which can be considered a true aphrodisiac, as it works directly on the genital organs as a tonic stimulant. For this purpose make a tea of 1 teaspoon herb to a cup of boiling water and leave to brew for 10 minutes. It can be toxic and cause liver damage so it may be safer to use it in incense to attract or to heighten sexual abandon. In his book *A Manual of Sex Magick*, Louis J Culling describes a drink made from dried Damiana leaves as a psychic aphrodisiac. And in *The Magical and Ritual Use of Herbs*, the companion book he gives a recipe for a cordial of Damiana and vodka. That can be used in Tantric and sex magic. (See chapter 3 Sex Magic)

The Maya considered asthma a disease that evil winds carried into the body, not only does it cause shortness of breath and depression, it can also make a person impotent and destroy all sexual desire. With the aid of damiana, however, a person afflicted with asthma can regain his/her joy of life; it also increases the flow of blood to the lower abdomen and swells sexual desire. Interestingly the Mayan healers were not the only ones who saw a connection between asthma and impotency or sexual desire, doctors and physicians from other traditions also arrived at similar insights. Damian was the patron saint of pharmacists and there was a Spanish missionary and Christian martyr named Damian.

Darnel

(Lolium temulentum) Bearded darnel is sometimes known as 'cheat', 'tare', is used by doctors to treat dizziness, insomnia, blood congestion, and stomach problems. It may also be used for skin problems like herpes, scurf, and sores. Darnel is a grass that if sprinkled with frankincense, myrrh and barley meal is reputed to be a sexual aid for women. This herb is poisonous in large quantities and is not to be used without medical direction

Date Palm

(Phoenix dactyifera) The date palm was probably cultivated in Mesopotamia some 8,000 thousand years ago, stuffed dates have a very erotic look to them. Preserved dates are by many gourmets believe to have erotic stimulus. They are rich in vitamins, and having the same calorific value as sirloin steak, it is not surprising that as this rather underrated fruit appears in many of the aphrodisiac recipes of the famous Arab physicians. Dates are rich in vitamins and have more calorific value than steak; they have been used in love feasts for thousands of years.

Deer Sperm

In ancient times, deer sperm was used as an ingredient in aphrodisiac concoctions. (Also see musk)

Diasatyrion

According to Venette, diasatyrion root could be taken morning and night with a little wine or milk, for a week to rejuvenate the sexual prowess of the older man. In inns in ancient Persia, now Iran, a viscous drink was sold the base of which was Satyrion. The Persians called it 'syrup of fox.'

Dill

(Anethum graveolens) Dill whose ruler is Mercury, was often used in the East as an ingredient in aphrodisiac meals and in magic. Culpeper maintained that dill was good for pains in the womb and used it for

good digestion. The seeds are used in love philtres and potions, particularly in mulled wine where it is reputed as an aphrodisiac. For this purpose you may also add a drop or two of the essential oil or an infusion of seeds to your bath to make you irresistible to the opposite sex. The oil also makes a good addition to any massage oil to be used by lovers. Michael Drayton, the English poet, refers to the stimulating effect of dill in love potions in the 1500s and much Roman herbal lore singles out dill as one of the most potent of all aphrodisiac plants.

Dita
(Alstonia scholaris) (Also see *Alstonia scholaris*) Dita is a tree that grows in Asia with large shiny leaves and white flowers. The bark has been used in medicine, for many ailments, and the seeds are used as an aphrodisiac. In ancient India the seeds were served in Tantric rituals for strengthening the erection and delaying orgasm.

Dog Stones
(See Satyrion)

Dong Quai
(Angelica sinensis; Angelica polymorpha) Dong quai is sometimes spelled dang gui or tang kuei. It is native to China and Japan, where is grows deep in mountain ravines, meadows and riverbanks. It is called Angelica as it was supposedly revealed by the Archangel Raphael as a gift with potent magical powers. It is widely used as a tonic for women because it contains oestrogen-like substances.

It may help to boost sexuality in women whose sex drive is low and is linked with menopausal symptoms, heavy periods, and menstrual cramps. It is said to increase blood circulation to the pelvis and regulate the menstrual cycle.

Dove
Dove's brains have been prepared by chefs as aphrodisiacs as part of love banquets.

Dragon's Blood
(Daemonorops draco) Ruler Mars, the resin of Dragon's Blood is used externally as a wash to promote healing and stop bleeding. Internally it is used for chest pains, post-partum bleeding, internal traumas, and menstrual irregularities. Dragon's blood is a plant used as a love charm; it was wrapped in paper and thrown in the fire, to the accompaniment of a rhyming couplet, "May he no pleasure or profit see, till he comes back again to me."

Drepang
(See sea slug)
Drumstick Tree
(Sirisa Albizzia lebbeck) The drumstick tree can grow up to 60 feet and is planted on roadsides for shade in India; it has pods full of brown flat seeds. A juice is made from the drumstick flowers which are used in recipes for many medicines including asthma and a treatment for insect bites. It is also regarded to promote virility.
Dudaim
(European Mandrake) Dudaim is the biblical term for mandrake; this root has been identified with Zizyphus, the Spina Christ of Linnaeus and is well known as an aphrodisiac. (Also see mandrake)
Dufz
A perfume used by Arabs as an aphrodisiac stimulant.
Durian
(Durio zibethinus) The durian tree produces hedgehog sized brown fruits, which are known variously as 'stink fruits' 'stink nuts' and 'tree cheese'. The fruit has a rotten stink and is not allowed to be carried on public transportation in many countries. The fresh ripe fruit has a reputation as an especially powerful aphrodisiac throughout Southeast Asia and is often used in folk medicine. The prickly fruit of the durian tree native to Borneo, Malaya, Thailand and the Philippines is a renowned aphrodisiac. An ancient Malay saying declares that when the durians fall, the sarongs rise.' The spherical fruit measure 15 to 20 cm in diameter an contain five oval compartments, each filled with a cream coloured, custard like pulp containing chestnut sized seeds. The pulp is edible and the seeds may be eaten if roasted. The durian has a pungent odour, which has been compared to that of strong cheese, but is mild and sweet to taste. It is so prized as an aphrodisiac that owners frequently sleep under the trees as harvest time, to protect their crop.
Dust to Dust
Among Bretons in France it was an old custom for the women after a religious service to gather the dust in the chapel and blow it over a reluctant lover, in the confident anticipation of the aphrodisiac effect of the action.

Echinacea

(Echinacea augustifolia, Echinacea purpurea also known as Purple coneflower) Echinacea is an herb indigenous to North America. Native Americans claim that it is vital to health enhancing resistance to infection such as the common cold. It reputedly can also help with loss of libido. The hydrosol can be used as a sexual wash and has immune boosting properties.

Echites

(Linnean herbarium) Also called Aquileus, because it is found in eagles nests, purple in colour, it contains another stone in it, found near ocean's shores and in Persia; conducive to generate love, Albertus Magnus, De Secretis Milierum.

Ecstasy

The love drug MDMA is derived from a substance present in the essential oils of nutmeg. MDMA exerts its primary effects in the brain on neurons that use the chemical serotonin to communicate with other neurons. The serotonin system plays an important role in regulating mood, aggression, sexual activity, sleep, and sensitivity to pain. MDMA can also be dangerous to health and, on rare occasions, lethal.

Eels

Like most marine life eels are said to possess aphrodisiac properties; often made into eel soup in love feasts.

Eggs

Eggs, especially free range eggs, contain steroidal substances that seem to enhance libido, the yolk of an egg in a small glass of cognac, drunk every morning has been popular as an aphrodisiac in France. In Morocco, love philtres are composed of yolk of egg and bedbugs. Many Oriental aphrodisiac dished can frequently contain eggs as an ingredient. Egg yolk is recommended by an Arab erotologist as a sexual stimulant. Another potent Arab dish is a mass of eggs fried in the butter and then cooked and soaked in honey on a slice of bread.

The Perfumed Garden says that he who eats the yolk of three eggs every day will be sexually invigorated; a similar stimulant is eggs boiled with pepper, cinnamon and myrrh. 'Go to work on an egg?' A historically potent drink consisted of eggs, milk salt, brandy and honey, compounded in an egg flip. This extract is from The Perfumed Garden. 'He who will feed for several days on eggs cooked with myrrh, cinnamon and pepper will find an increased vigour in his erections and in his capacity for coition'.

Elecampane
(Inula helenium) Elecampane, ruler Mercury, is used mixed with vervain and mistletoe to make a love powder. It was recommended by Culpeper as an aid in regulating women's problems and for digestive and urinary problems.

Endive
(Cichorium endiva) Endive was used as a love charm by witches in Germany. Endive like a number of similar plants; is both esculent and reputed to have aphrodisiac properties.

Epena
(Anadenanthera peregrine) Epena is a mimosa like tree from the tropical South American rain forests. Its bark is dark with coarse thorns; it has small flowers like grapes and long pods with dark brown seeds.

The natives of the Orinoco basin used the seeds to go into a psychedelic trance. It is also known as Epena, yopa and cahoba, and used by shamans to contact their spirit guides for healing. It has a reputed aphrodisiac power and can increase sexual vigour, the Indians use it as snuff but it can be smoked.

Ephedra
(Ephedra sinensis) There are varieties of ephedra that grow worldwide from the Himalayas to the Andes. It has tiny creamy white flowers and can thrive in extreme climatic conditions. It has been used in natural remedies for over 5,000 years and was known as ma-huang. It has a stimulating and reviving effect on the body when used in teas. Itwas also considered an aphrodisiac.

190

Eryngo

(Eryngium maritimum) Also known as sea holly, sea hulver and sea holme, the testicle-shaped root of this plant was extraordinarily popular in Regency Britain as an aphrodisiac. It has the appearance of a thistle with like flowers, its virtue lies in the fleshy root. For centuries it was used as a powerful aphrodisiac. Demand for the candied eryngo was so impressive among the less active bucks that one entrepreneur opened an eryngo factory in Colchester. In Shakespeare's *The Merry Wives of Windsor* Falstaff mentions the root; "Hail kissing comfits, and snow eryngoes."

The root has been candied to strengthen the genitals and give potency; in this form the Arabs knew it as an invigorating sexual stimulant.

Dioscorides, an army physician who flourished in the 1st century said; "Who lewdly dances at a midnight ball, for hot eryngoes and fat oysters call".

Euphorbium

(Euphorbia Millii & Euphorbia Lactea) A gum resin derived from a plant that is indigenous to North and to South Africa, according to Sinibaldus, it is mentioned by Avicenna as an aphrodisiacal aid. Euphorbium is a much used homeopathic remedy primarily used for asthma.

False Unicorn

(Chamaelirium luteum; Helonias dioica) False unicorn is a perennial herb from North American which is also known as 'blazing star' and 'fairy wind'. It is chewed by Native American women to help prevent miscarriage and is also said to have aphrodisiac properties.

Feet

Feet are sexy, it is not necessary to be a foot fetishist to enjoy the erotic possibilities of your feet. The soles of your feet are ticklish because they are well served with nerve endings; the ancient art of Reflexology uses this in a healthy and relaxing way to balance the body A gentle foot massage can also be used to stimulate hidden erotic triggers and this art has long been used by oriental Corsicans.

Fennel

(Foeniculum vulgare) Ruler Mercury, a fragrant plant used in sauces and believed to inspire sexual provocations; a Hindu prescription for sexual vigour and at the same time a preservative of health. Juice of the plant mixed with honey, ghee, liquorice and sugar is described as holy, partaking of the extract as nectar. Fennel soup is a dish used in some Mediterranean regions reputed to stimulate desire. Fennel has great magical affinity with the serpent deities, it can thus be very helpful in the gentle release of kundalini energies, and fennel can also be used in small doses in love potions and if eaten with eel was reputed to promote strong lustful feelings. If carried in your charm bag fennel has the power to make all your utterances sound believable and sincere. Eating fennel is said to stimulate the genitals and arouse desire. Even the dew gathered from the leaves of fennel was believed to have magical powers, including the property of strengthening both physical and magical sight clairvoyance.

Sow Fennel or Hogs Fennel

Ruler mercury *Culpeper's Herbal* recommends sow fennel to ease women in childbirth and for bladder problems and there is some belief it aids women to become sexually receptive again after childbirth.

Fenugreek

(Trigonella foenum-graecum) Fenugreek grows in Kashmir and the Punjab but is cultivated throughout India. Fenugreek seeds are considered aphrodisiac, tonic and cleansing. For women they are also an emmenagogue, (a substance which causes menstruation) and it also has a diuretic effect.

Figs

(Moraceae Ficus) There are a genus of about 800 species of woody trees, shrubs and vines in the family of figs. The fig is considered sensual and erotic for when the fruit is slit open, the juicy, pale pink flesh is apparently reminiscent of the female genitals. In some cultures

figs are eaten at weddings and thrown at newlyweds in the place of rice. Figs were anciently associated with phallic symbolism, according to Plutarch, the Greek biographer and philosopher. The fig was also symbolic of the lingam (penis) and the yoni (vagina). The French expression 'faire la figue' means to make the obscene sexual gesture with two fingers and a thumb. This gesture was well-known in the antique 'lupanaria' of the Romans. The fig is mentioned frequently in the Bible and is included in the Garden of Eden. It is a traditional food in the Jewish Passover celebration. The fig tree figures in the founding of great cultures and religions. Romulus and Remus, the founders of Rome, were suckled by a she-wolf under a fig tree, which later, in the time of Pliny, was revered as a sacred tree. While sitting under a fig tree, Siddhartha Gautama had the revelation that formed the foundations of Buddhism. Figs have been prized for both medicinal and dietary value. Mithridates, the Greek king of Pontus (120-63 B.C.), heralded figs as an antidote for all ailments and instructed his physicians to consider its uses as a medicine. Pliny of Rome (62-113) said "Figs are restorative. They are the best food that can be eaten by those who are brought low by fatigue, long sickness and are on the way to recovery including sexual recovery. They increase the strength of young people, preserve the elderly in better health and make them look younger with fewer wrinkles". The early Greeks so highly prized figs that it was considered an honour to bestow the foliage and fruit. In the original Olympic Games, winning athletes were crowned with fig wreaths and given figs to eat. The festival of the Dionysian was anciently celebrated in a popular and lively manner. A wine jar was carried round and also a vine branch, then someone brought forward a goat, and another basket filled with figs; sounds like a great party to me!

Fish

Many aphrodisiac recipes contain seafood and this is common to all cultures and periods of history. A spicy fish stew is recommended by such varied authorities as a Hindu sage and a Roman seducer. Fish is traditionally considered a powerful and unfailing erotic aid, particularly on account of the presence of phosphates and iodine. In the ancient Middle East certain cults had piscine deities, or deities with fish attributes of various kinds. The Roman poet chanted the praise of river and sea fish. Ausonius, for instance, has a poem on the Moselle life, about 150 verses being devoted to barbel, trout, turbot, and other fish are associated with that river. Catherine 11 of Russia was childless by her husband, the grandson of Peter the Great, she was told by her Chancellor that the Empire needed an heir. She ordered her chef to prepare a feast of caviar and fine sturgeon, and commanded  an officer of the guard, Saltikoff, to be invited to dinner. The outcome was a healthy and acceptable heir to the throne. According to Apuleius, fish were used as love charms; a fish bone is often included in magical sachets and lucky amulets. In Egypt the aphrodisiac virtues of fish were so generally recognized that priests were forbidden to eat fish when they had to remain celebrate. Fish in antiquity was credited with special aphrodisiac virtues and efficacy in exciting women, a suggested explanation was that Venus herself was born in the sea. Her Greek name, Aphrodite, is associated with the Greek term *aphros*, which means foam.

Flea-Wort

(Psyllium) Ruler Saturn. Well known as a traditional aphrodisiac. The sap of this plant, according to Pliny the Elder, author of Historia Naturalis, was an effective means of securing the birth of a male child. The parents drank the sap three times daily while fasting for forty days.

Flowers

The giving of flowers has aphrodisiac effects on women; this is particularly true of lilies of the valley, gardenia, frangipani and roses (red roses for passion, pink for love and white for platonic love.) Many kinds of flowers are used in love spells and sachets. Glazed flower petals can also be used as garnish on dishes in our love feast.

Fly Agaric

(Amanita Muscaria var Flavivolvata) Fly agaric is a mushroom which grows in forests that have been thinned. Fly agaric has long been popular and is mentioned in many legends and myths. Some cultures have associated it with the gods or devils; in India these are one and the same. The mushroom is eaten by shamans and clairvoyants and used as an aphrodisiac and for healing and prophecy.

Fly Agaric produces a substance that produces hallucinations, like mescaline, and also induces sexual intensity with corresponding

194

heightening of sensory channels and the olfactory and visual senses a general condition of a kind of love intoxication. This hallucinogenic drug is very dangerous and must not be used without proper medical or psychiatric controls.

Fo-ti or he shou wu

(Polygonum multiform) Fo-ti, also known as 'he shou wu', is a perennial climber native to Central and Southern China. It is one of the oldest Chinese tonic herbs used to prevent aging. According to legend an elderly impotent and childless man, Mr He left his village and went into the mountains over 1000 years ago. Mr He survived for several years by eating herbs, fruit and grains and the root of fo-ti. When he retuned to his village his friends and family did not recognize him. The shou wu had also restored his virility allowing him to father numerous children and live to the age of over 130 years. Fo-ti is famous for its rejuvenating and revitalizing properties, it is widely used by millions of men and women in the East as a general restorative, to promote fertility, sexual function and boost a low sex drive.

Fo-Ti-Tieng

(Hydrocotyle asiatica minor) This perennial plant has purple flowers and a flat rounded and purplish red fruit that comes from Asia and is popular as a vegetable in Sri Lanka and is the fabled 'elixir of long life'. The plant is also known as 'gotu kola', Asian marsh pennywort, bevilacqua and gotu kola. It is reputed that the leaves taken daily prolong life and act as an aphrodisiac. Fo-Ti-Tieng was used widely in Sri Lanka and China. Li Chung Yun a famous Chinese herbalist who died in 1933 had reportedly been born in 1677 and died at the age of 256; he had out-lived twenty four wives. It is also called 'shoo koo' in Chinese and is renowned as an extender of life and vitality. It was used by the Taoist and was said to be a secret of immortally and was used in sex rites to enable men to give their partners several orgasms.

Frangipane-Cream

A pastry, consisting of Frangipane, spices and almonds, is suggested as a sexual aid in an Italian erotic cookery book.

Frankincense

(N.O Burseraceae) Frankincense, also known as olibanum, has been frequently mentioned in association with erotic themes in sexual manuals and in the bible. A good essential oil for romantic massage blends. It is a stimulant, but seldom used now internally, though formerly was in great repute. Pliny mentions it as an antidote to hemlock. Avicenna (tenth century) recommends it for tumours, ulcers, vomiting, dysentery and fevers. In China it is used for leprosy.

Frog

According to medical writer, Alexander Benedictus, dried frog powder induced a disgust of sexual activities. The bones of frogs were used among the Romans as aphrodisiacs. Frogs legs have been considered a culinary delicacy in many countries especially France. Frog's legs were called by Norman Douglas a 'noble aphrodisiac.'

Place a live frog in an anthill and leave until the ants have cleaned the bones then take the heart shaped bone and the hook shaped bone; keep the first yourself but hook the second in the clothes of a loved one. (African American folklore.)

Fruit

Among fruits reputed to have stimulating qualities are bananas, fresh figs, peaches, cherries and grapes. (Also see fruit individually by name) Sophisticates often insert into the vagina fruits such as strawberries or cherries, or an orange section or apple slice dipped in honey, thereupon sucking or drawing them out again, and eating them with much enjoyment. The banana is classically used in this way. 'Not recommended for persons with false teeth.' G Legman, Oragenitalis, 1969.

Galanga

(Kaempferia galanga) Galanga is used in Malaysia and Indonesia as an herbal medicine and an aphrodisiac. The plant thrives in the tropical rain forests of Asia. Galanga as a root is used among Arabs as an aphrodisiac, a mixture of galanga, cubebs, sparrow wort, cardamoms, nutmeg, gillyflowers, Indian thistle, laurel seeds, cloves and Persian pepper is made into a tonic drink. Taken twice daily, morning and evening, in pigeon broth preceded and followed by water. The result was apparently a very effective aphrodisiac.

Galangol

(Alpinia officinarum) In China this ginger like plant is harvested for its medicinal properties. The Arabian physician Ibn-al-Baytar attributed aphrodisiac properties. The pungent root according to Mattioli "...it stimulates bodily lusts". According to German folk medicine it is if a person eats the root or even lays it on his penis he can have sex twelve times in succession.

Gall

The gall of a jackal, among Arabs was used as an aphrodisiac. It is specifically recommended as an ointment for this purpose by the Sheik Nefzawi, author of *The Perfumed Garden.*

Game

Game of most kinds, goose, duck, quail and pheasant are all credited with being stimulants and arouse erotic awareness.

Garlic or Garlick

(Allium sativum) Ruler Mars, eating garlic can improve feelings of wellbeing and boost sex drive and for magical purposes. It is reputed by many to have aphrodisiac value, according to medical authority, from both European and Oriental erotologists. Garlic is mentioned by Culpeper as a tonic and said "… it will add fuel to the fire."

197

Among the Ainu of Japan garlic is considered in the same category as the ancient Greek nectar and ambrosia of the gods.

The Romans consecrated it to Ceres, the Goddess of Fertility and made a love cocktail from pressed garlic juice and coriander. Many old books say that garlic leads to lascivious behaviour. Every summer the Isle of Wight has a garlic festival and they even have garlic flavoured ice cream.

Ghee

In Hindu custom, ghee, which is clarified butter, is considered as an aphrodisiac. An ancient Hindu manual on erotology suggests boiled ghee, drunk in the morning, in the spring time, as a healthful strengthening beverage.

Gillyflower

Gillyflower is a clove scented plant used as a condiment. It is also an alleged aphrodisiac.

Ginger

(Zingiber officinale Roscoe) Ginger is a perennial, tropical plant native to the jungles of South East Asia. Used in many recipes, always use the fresh root. Madam du Barry used ginger in many dishes including omelettes and stuffed meat and fowls as an aphrodisiac. Ginger is one of the oldest medicinal spices and aphrodisiacs known. It was taken regularly by Confucius the great philosopher of the 5th and 4th centuries BCE, who helped to make it popular in China for medical purposes and as an aphrodisiac. Ginger is a warming energizing spice that can increase blood circulation and liven up your sex drive.

Ginger was mentioned in Scheherazade's *Thousand and One Nights*, as an aphrodisiac. Asian medical systems consider the root 'hot' it brings heat or fire (agni) into the body and thus excites the sexual organs as well. It is often used in love potions.

In Turkish, Indian, Arabian and other Oriental love recipes ginger is frequently present as an ingredient in amatory concoctions, often too taken by mouth along with honey and pepper. Ginger is warming and makes an excellent essential oil for circulation, arthritis conditions,

198

baths and foot baths for cold feet. In *The Perfumed Garden* ginger was recommended as an external stimulant. It could be massaged into the abdomen or chewed with cubeb berries and spices and then the saliva was applied to the genitals; also ginger honey can be applied in this way and then sucked off. Hot stuff hey?

Use ginger in sachets and philtres where you are more interested in sexual passion than romantic love, it works well as part of a seduction spice mix and is a very effective ingredient in any love philtre.

Ginkgo

(Ginkgo biloba) The Ginkgo biloba, or maidenhair tree, is one of the oldest known plants. It seems to have remained unchanged during the last 200 million years and is often described as a living fossil. It boosts blood circulation to brain, hands, feet and genitals by stopping cell fragments in the blood (platelets) from clumping together. Research show that it can improve blood flow to the penis and help strengthen and maintain an erection. Ginkgo is one of the most popular health supplements in Europe today where it helps to improve memory and concentration and is used in treating dementia. It was considered sacred in China and Japan and is planted on Taoist, Buddhist and Shinto temple grounds. Since ancient times, the sacred tree has great importance as a healing plant in Chinese medicine. Everybody should take Ginkgo biloba every day to improve their memory and circulation of the body.

Ginseng

(Panax ginseng; P. quinquefolium) Ginseng usually referred to as Chinese, Korean or Asian ginseng, is a perennial plant native to North Eastern China, Eastern Russia and North Korea; it is now rare in the wild. Ginseng is a true pro-sexual supplement and adaptagen, prized as an aphrodisiac, sexual enhancer and fertility aid. Ginseng can be grated and eaten in soups and salads, dried and powdered to use in teas and tablets. Ginseng is one of the most widely available aphrodisiacs with an impressive

list of its supposed benefits. The Chinese have revered this plant for thousands of years. Like mandrake, the most potent ginseng roots are said to be shaped like the human body. The Chinese believe that even better results were obtained when the root was dug up at midnight during a full moon. (Also see chapter 9 Ginseng)

Goat

Goat is included in a Hindu prescription for achieving sexual activity, beverages are prepared with the testicle of a goat or ram boiled in milk and sugar. The goat was associated with the goddess Aphrodite on account of its amorous tendencies, also to Dionysus the god of fertility and procreation. Pan the sylvan deity who was attended by satyrs of highly sexual proclivities, was represented invariably with goat's feet and as the special protector of goats. Dioscorides, 1st century, A.D. Greek physician extolled the virtues of goat's milk; he recommended cabbage, steeped in goats, milk as an arouser agent.

A 14th century remedy for impotence that has been contrived through a magic spell is as follows: Burdock seeds, crushed in a mortar, add the left testis of a three year old goat, a pinch of powder from the back hairs of a white dog. The hairs must be cut on the first day of the new moon and burned on the seventh day. Infuse all these items in a bottle half filled with brandy. Leave uncorked for 21 days, so that it may receive the astral influence. On the 21st day, as the moon rises, cook the entire mixture until a thick consistency is reached. Then add four drops of crocodile semen and pass the concoction through a filter. Gather up the resultant liquid and apply to the genitals. The application will have marvellous effect immediately. Since crocodiles are rare in Europe the semen of certain dogs may be used. It is said that Cleopatra believed in this substitution since dogs were able to avoid extermination by the crocodiles on the banks of the Nile. In any case this experiment, says the tradition has always been successful if one used dogs or crocodiles. (If anyone decides to try this please let me know the results!)

The sicinnis is a Greek erotic dance which represented the jumping of goats; it was associated with the sensual ways of satyrs. In the West Indies goat curry with spices is known to be a sexual arouser in some circles and goat testes are sex in voodoo sex spells in Tahiti.

Goose

The goose has often traditionally been seen as a symbol of potency. A passage Petronius, author of the Satyricon, described the reaction as a result of killing a goose as of killing the love and passion in a relationship. Goose tongues were known for the aphrodisiac qualities and recommended by the Roman poet Ovid. Goose grease is often used in ointments and salves; mixed with herbs in herbal health treatments.

Gotu Kola

(Centella asiatica or Hydrocotyle asiatica) Gotu kola is an herbaceous perennial plant native to India, China, Indonesia, Australia and the South Pacific. It is reputed to increase longevity and is also referred to as the fountain of youth. Legend claims that gotu kola was one of the herbs used by a Chinese herbalist, Li Ching Yun, who reputedly lived to the age of 256. It is one of the most important Ayurvedic herbs, known as brahmi prescribed for many ailments. It aids sex drive in those who need a general energy boost, tonic and whose low sex drive is linked with worry or stress.

Gossypion

(From Latin *gossypion*, cotton plant) Gossypion is a tree whose juice, according to a medieval writer named Andreas Cisalpinus, was an esteemed aphrodisiac.

Gourou

(Paullinia cupana) Gourou is the native African term for the kola nut; this is really a large chestnut, like a horse chestnut. The natives of Senegal and the Sudan chew the Gourou with relish, a noted anthropologist says that it produces a sort of general nervous excitement, which sensibly increased all the physical faculties, including sexual prowess. At the great bamboulas and fetes the Gourou is much valued and helps when there is strenuous or amorous work to be done. Kola is now admitted into European therapeutics and is used for restoring lost strength and stimulating the forces of the body. It contains a higher abundance of caffeine and theobromine than the finest teas and coffees.

Grapes and Grape Juice

(Vitis vinifera) The grapevine is one of the world's oldest cultivated plants. Its original home was in Asia Minor but grows today throughout the world. Since ancient times grapes have been eaten as a fruit, made to raisins, or pressed into wine. Grapes have a stimulatory value; anciently grapes were associated with the god Dionysus, deity of fertility and procreation and grape juice has a reputed aphrodisiac virtue. Wine and alcohol lowers the inhibitions but too much alcohol dampens the sexual urge.

201

Guarana

(Papavaer somniferum) The Guaraná liana is a climbing shrub with divided compound leaves and yellow flowers that grows in the hot, humid and tropical rain forests of the Amazon. It has chestnut like fruits that have been called the 'fruits of youth' by the locals. For centuries the Indians of the Amazon have collected the seeds and used them to prepare a very stimulating drink, which has a very stimulating and aphrodisiac effect; it is also used as an appetite suppressant and is often  found in slimming preparations. It has also been used as body makeup and was used in Tantric rites and sex magic; the herb was mixed with oil and ashes as painted on the body for seduction purposes and to protect from psychic disturbances.

Guayaca Wood

(Guayacum sanctum) The Guayaca is an evergreen tree that grows in Central America. Its wood is known as lignum vitae 'wood of life'. The Indians of Central America use the wood to manufacture hunting bows because of its hardness. The wood is considered an aphrodisiac and its hardness is supposed to transfer to the penis.

Guinea Fowl

Roasted guinea fowl has been a favourite dish among French gourmets intent on sexual seduction.

Hair

Hair has often been used in aphrodisiacs. One 13th century remedy required taking the private member of a wolf and the hair from his cheeks or eyebrows and the hair of his beard, burn it all and give it to the person you desire in a drink; they will then be consumed with desire.

Halibut

This fish is considered to have stimulating aphrodisiac properties.

Hare Soup

The hare has a reputation of exciting desire and hare soup is credited with a particular aphrodisiacal value.

Haricot Beans

Haricot beans are considered to have highly stimulating aphrodisiac properties.

Harmine

(Banisteria caapi) Harmine is a drug chemically related to mescaline, which is very hazardous. The plant grows in the foothills of the Andes and in the Amazon basin in South America. The leaves of the plant are utilized to make a greenish infusion that contains the alkaloid harmine. This alkaloid is also obtained from the seeds of the Wild Rue, which grows in Australia, New Zealand and South America. Harmine is a drug that stimulates the brain and produces strange visual hallucinations of an erotic nature.

Hashish

(Cannabis indica) The Indian hemp plant is chewed, smoked and drunk. The term assassin is derived from the Arabic *hashishin*, 'hemp eaters', that is, drug addicts. Moroccans used it as a popular aphrodisiac compound consisting of hashish, acorns, honey, sweet almonds,

sesame, butter, cantharides and nuts. Hashish has a demoralising effect, removing inhibitions and replacing them by emotional excitement. The sense of moral responsibility is lost, together with all will and self-power. The aphrodisiac effect stems from the creation of such excitement and abandonment and loss of restraints and moral sensibilities. The stimulation is local occurring in the genitals and giving a sensitising effect. In the Orient hashish is often taken to precede sexual relations.

In the case of marihuana, as inhibitions are removed, the smoker becomes highly suggestible and may incline towards sexual expression but long term use can have the opposite effects and the user will become morose and sexually inept. Theophile Gautier, the 19th century French poet and novelist, was a hashish addict. He said that "a hashish addict would not lift a finger, or anything else, for the most beautiful maiden in Verona". Other noteworthy men who have succumbed to the hashish habit were Gerard de Nerval, Honore de Balzac, Alexandre Dumas and Charles Baudelaire in France and Charles Lamb in England. Hashish and marihuana were very popular for hippies and the free love era of the sixties, it has also been widely used in the religion of the Rastafarian.

Hedgehog

In Roman times the genital organs of the hedgehog and the wolf were among ingredients used in one aphrodisiac concoction. In Gypsy folklore roasted hedgehog is considered an aphrodisiac especially if eaten with a wild herb salad that includes wild lettuce and young dandelion leaves. *The Perfumed Garden* refers to a sheik Nefzawi who enumerates on some fifty synonyms for the virile member of various species. Rabelais, in his *Gargantua et Pantagruel*, offers a similar bizarre list and much modern French slang is likewise rich in erotic synonyms.

Hedysarum

(Alhagi mannifera) Hedysarum sometimes known as 'Manna Tree,' 'Liquorice Root' or 'Camel Thorn' is used for increasing vigour. An Oriental erotic text advises drinking the juices of hedysarum gangeticum, the kuli and the kshirka plants in milk.

Hemlock

(Conium maculatum) Ruler Saturn. Hemlock was much used in ancient times but is considered too dangerous today. It grows in the hedges of

Europe and is a member of the umbelliferae family. Conium comes from the Greek *conos*, a top, and allusion being the giddiness of the head caused by hemlock. It was considered a deadly poison; Socrates, the Greek philosopher, was condemned to drink a cup of hemlock, from which he died, in 399 BCE.

The Greek biographer Plutarch describes the medicinal properties of the herb and its poisonous effect. In the 18th century hemlock was used for treating cancer, syphilis and ulcers. Hemlock grown in the foothills of the Caucasus and in the Crimea, being inert, was eaten by cattle but in other parts of Europe it is actively poisonous. Formerly hemlock was termed *Herba Benedict*, the blessed herb, because "where the root is in the house the devil can do no harm, and if anyone should carry the plant about on his person, no venomous beast can harm him." As early as the 10th century the herb was used widely in AngloSaxon medicine and in the Tyrol on May Day, it was the custom to smoke out witches by burning bundles of black and red spotted hemlock. Hemlock mixed in a drink was anciently used as a means of destroying men's virility.

Hemp

(Cannabis sativa) Ruler Saturn. Hemp is a dioecious plant, the male plants, with the stamens, is smaller and more delicate than the female, which is used as a drug. Hemp was cultivated as a food and source of fibre and is one of humanity's oldest cultivated plants. Hemp has throughout history been used to dull pain and prolong active life. Marijuana and hashish, together with alcohol are the most important inebriants to humankind. It is considered an active aphrodisiac as it eases pain, lowers inhibitions and relaxes the body to enrich the erotic experience. Hemp was used by Turks as pills consisting of hemp buds, Muscat nuts, saffron and honey as an aphrodisiac. (Also see Hashish and Cannabis)

Henbane

(Hyoscyamus niger) Ruler Saturn, some astrologers put this as an herb of Jupiter. Henbane is also known as hyoscyamus, bean of the hog and more commonly called hogsbean. A drug is obtained from the flowering plant, which grows in England and in Europe. The plant has large, sea green leaves and bell shaped, creamy coloured, flowers streaked with purple. It has a heavy oppressive aroma and is clammy to the touch. It is eaten by hogs and pigs but is a deadly poison for humans. Both Dioscorides and the Roman medical writer Celsus were

familiar with henbane. In France the plant was called Jusquiame; in Germany it was known as the 'Devils' Eye'. In rural areas of Europe it was smoked like tobacco but it produced convulsions and hallucinations; it was also widely used in witchcraft and black magic. Witches were said to have used the plant in preparing madness-inducing love potions. Until recently henbane came from Egypt and was known as Egyptian Henbane. In the Nile Delta it is called sakran 'the drunkard' it is also an aphrodisiac and in large doses quite deadly.

Henna

The pulverized leaves and twigs of henna are used as a hair dye in many European countries and as skin decoration in India and the East. Among Arabs it is believed that henna rubbed on the fingers, skull and feet produced an aphrodisiac reaction. Indian women are decorated with henna on hands and feet on their wedding day for this reason.

Herissah

Herissah in the Orient, is a mixture consisting of mutton and flour, seasoned with red pepper and is believed to be a sexual stimulant.

Herring

Herring, like many fish, is considered an aphrodisiac food; particularly the rolled raw herring found in Holland and Northern Europe.

Hibiscus

(Japa kusume/Hibiscus Rosa-sinensis) Hibiscus originates from India but now grows in gardens all over the world. Hibiscus flowers can be used with love incenses, or carried as a love potion. In Ayurvedic literature hibiscus flowers are known to have anti-fertility effects and are used for birth control and as a treatment for menorrhagia. It is also used to cure impotence and to promote virility.

Hindu Ointment

Hindu ointment was an aphrodisiac ointment, recommended by the *Kama Sutra*, the Hindu erotic manual and contains the following; Tabernamontana coronaria, xanthochymus pichorius, ghee and honey, blue lotus, *mesna roxhurghii* and *nelumbrium speciosum.*

Hindu Powder

Hindu powder is an amatory enticement; eating the powder of nelumbrium speciosum, the blue lotus and the *mesna roxburghii*, with ghee and honey.

Hippocras Aphrodisiac
According to folk tradition a potent sexual stimulant consisting of red burgundy wine with a mixture of ginger, crushed cinnamon, cloves, vanilla in white sugar. Rabelais in *Gargantua and Pantagruel* refers to its beneficial value for sexual prowess.

Hippocrates
Hippocrates, the most famed Greek physician, who died in the same year as Socrates, stated that a predisposing cause of impotence among the ancient Scythians was the wearing of tight breeches. Arab erotologists express similar views about more modern conditions and sexual experts today say don't wear tight pants/trousers for long periods.

Hippomanes
Hippomanes is a protuberance that appears on a colt's head at birth and is bitten off by the mare. Hippomanes was used in an ancient Roman potion as an aphrodisiac. It was as large as a fig, black in colour and derived its name from a Greek expression meaning horse madness. Virgil, Ovid, Pliny the Elder and Juvenal all describe hippomanes as an excrescence on a new born colt. In the *Aeneid*, Virgil, listing the operations of a witch priestess says, "She has sprinkled water, so she feigns from a Avernus spring and she is getting green downy herbs cropped by moonlight with brazen shears, whose sap is the milk of deadly poison and the love charm torn from the brow of the new born foal, ere the mother could snatch it; " An alternative meaning for hippomanes is that it is a fluid that trickles from the mare that attracts the stallion; this also is used in charms and love rites. Pausanias, a Greek traveller, has likewise something to say of hippomanes, one of these horses the Aelians declare may have been made by a magician, of brass, into which metal he had previously infused the hippomanes. Which possessed the power of exciting horses to a mad desire for coition?

Honey
Galen a Greek of the 2nd century A.D and court physical to the Emperor Marcus Aurelius, recommended as an effective aphrodisiac a glass of thick honey, taken before bedtime, together with the consumption of almonds and one hundred grains of the pine tree. The recipe was to be followed for three consecutive nights. A compound of honey, pepper and ginger is also recommended as an aphrodisiac by

13th century Arab physician Avicenna. In many an Oriental dish honey is a frequent ingredient. Honey contains bee pollen which may account for its reputed pro-sexual effect Honey was widely used in poultices applied to the lingam (male member) to increase its size in ancient India, and mixed with crocodile dung, olive oil and lemon juice for use as a contraceptive barrier by women.

Honey can also be used as a lubricant and a delicious introduction to the pleasures of oral sex. An erotic game called 'The tree ' in Japan where some lovers prefer to lick honey or yogurt from one another's naked bodies; while doing so they might reflect that 'lechery' comes from the word for 'licking.' Honey has often been used in erotic literature to lubricate the sexual organs and add interest to the tongue. In Arabia honey and yogurt are often used on the male or females' genitals as a prelude to oral sex.

According to the Roman poet Ovid, author of the *Ars Amatoria*, honey was a great aphrodisiac. Hydromel is a beverage consisting of honey and water, once taken as an aphrodisiac. It is said that if you put a woman who's struggling to conceive on bee pollen, you can pretty much guarantee a result within two to three months. The belief is that pollen increases the biological value of the egg, restores and rejuvenates natural hormonal substances and can increase sexual stamina.

Honeysuckle

(Lonicera japonica) In some folk history maidens once slept with this strongly scented flower under their pillows to arouse prophetic dreams of the delights that they could hope to enjoy when they were no longer maidens.

Hops

(Humulus lupulus) Ruler Mars. Despite their macho connotation; an excess of hops affects the body's hormonal balance and can have a feminising effect on men. Men who have worked in beer-making, for example, have been known to grow breasts due to an overdose of the female hormone oestrogen.

Horny Goat Weed

(Epimedium sagittatum) Horny goat weed grows wild in China and is traditionally known as 'lusty goat herb' and 'yin yang huo', it is popular in the East but not so often used in the west. It is reputed to make goats fornicate after eating it and is used to treat impotence and lowered fertility in men. It is said to dilate blood vessels in the penis

and increase blood flow, improve erections and boost waning libido; it can also improve the female sex drive. The exact way it works is still unclear but it is believed to increase testosterone and levels of the brain chemicals required for sexual arousal, it also contains a flavonoid called 'icarrin' which is thought to help with erectile function.

Horseradish

(Armoracia rusticana) Used in Europe as a condiment, horseradish is reputed to have a stimulating sexual value. Horseradish was used in many cultures. The root is similar in appearance to a penis and is said to help with sexual exhaustion and general fatigue.

Horsetail

(Equisetum myriochaetum) Ruler Saturn. Horsetail is indigenous to Central American rain forests. Fresh segments of the stalk are made into teas for treating many ailments. The Lacandon Indians make a tea from fresh segments specifically for aphrodisiac purposes, which is said to improve hardness and stamina of the male sexual organ. Culpeper said; "used as a wash it eases the swelling heat and inflammations of the fundament, or privy parts on men and women."

Hypericum

(Hypericum perforatum) Hypericum is a perennial shrub found in many parts of the world, especially Europe and the United States. It was named Hyperikon by Hippocrates, the father of modern medicine, a name which literally meant 'above an icon' as sprigs of it were used to drive away evil spirits. It is also called St John's Wort, from the Knights of St John of Jerusalem who used it as a salve during the Crusades. Hypericum has bright yellow flowers and small oval leaves, it has been used for over 2,000 years to treat depression, low esteem and sleep problems. It is said to boost the level of the feel good hormones in the body and to aid in low sex drive.

Iboga

(Tabemanghe iboga) This bush grows in the Congo and West African rain forests; the shrub has white flowers that have pink spots and a berry with seeds. It has been used as a fetish plant and is well known by West African cults and sacred societies as a sacramental plant. The root is also considered to be one of the strongest African aphrodisiacs. The root is often combined with yohimbe bark in aphrodisiac potions. Ibogene is a drug obtained from a plant ibogo tabenanthe or cheha edulis; it's indigenous to the Yemen in Arabia. Ibogene is also markedly anti-sexual in its effects and certain native tribes use it as a beverage for this purpose. It is a drug that can enable sorcerers to visit the spirit world and cult leaders eat ibogo root when they wish to seek advice from dead ancestors. It has been used in ritual by the Tantric Buddhists and in sex magic with the order Templi Orientis, an 800 year old Masonic order based in Germany.

Indian Aloe

(Aloe indica) Aloe has large fleshy leaves and is native to eastern and southern Africa some species are found in India. Used as an emmenagogue and promoter of virility the fresh juice is a tonic and to help penile inflammation and skin complaints.

Indian Kudju

(Vidari Ipomoea digitata) Indian kudju is a climber with a woody stem, pink flowers and hairy brown seeds that grows in the Himalayas and Nepal. It is used as a promoter of semen, an aphrodisiac and general tonic.

Intestines
The intestines of some fish and birds were used as aphrodisiacs among the Romans.

Iporuro
(Alchornea floribunda) Iporuro is a shrub that is native to the Amazon. Its bark is harvested in the dry season when it contains a number of active ingredients including yohimbine. Yohimbine is a powerful treatment for impotence and the Tikuna Indians use iporuru to both increase the fertility of females and to treat male erectile dysfunction. It is taken fairly widely by older men as a general tonic and as an aphrodisiac.

Italian Soup
An Italian soup recipe, reputed to have aphrodisiac qualities, contains calves heel, crayfish, carrots, celery and shallots. Much Italian cookery has aphrodisiac stimulus; particularly foods like peppers, truffles and various other roots and herbs.

Jangida
(Withania somniferum) This bushy plant grows in South Asia and has small bell flowers and red fruit. The plant was used in Vedic magical rites and in Ayurvedic medicine. Chinese medicine used it as a curative and as an aphrodisiac. Love drinks made from the fruit are said to promote sexual vitality and to arouse any person and make them acquiescent.

Jasmine
(Jasminum, Yellow Gelsemium) Ruler Jupiter. Jasmine is known to the Hindu poets as 'Moonlight of the Grove'. This is a flower with one of the richest and most beautiful of fragrances. It is used mainly in the form of an exotic essential oil which can be very expensive if pure,

though there are synthetic jasmines available. This is not really surprising when you consider that it takes around 8,000 hand-picked flowers to make a single drop of this gorgeous oil. Jasmin is said to be a powerful aid in love spells, added to your bath water or burnt as incense. Mixed with orris root and rose petals it makes a very good love bath. There are just three different plants, with roots that stick up and catch sand and form islands. The roots look like legs sticking up, thus 'man grove.'

Juniper

(Juniperus communis) Ruler the Sun. Juniper is a shrub that produces fleshy berries of purple colour and pungent taste. It yields oil that is used medicinally and in massage. The berries are steeped in water and the juice is drunk, John Gerarde, author of *Herball,* 1633 recommends it as a wholesome drink. Juniper is also credited with the virtue of maintaining an erection and giving youthful ardour to tired men. The berries of the shrub were used as an ingredient in cordials and formerly juniper was considered of medicinal value by herbalists. It was also used in magic, especially in love charms and philtres. Juniper is often associated with Juno Virginensis the Roman goddess who presided over the consummation of marriage. In North America, Native American tribes made a tea from juniper berries which they drank as a contraceptive.

Justicia

(Justicia pectorialis) This plant grows in the open clearings all over Central America and in the Caribbean, where it is considered an aphrodisiac. The entire plant is dried in the sun and made into a powder. The powder is taken like snuff or smoked with cannabis.

Karengro

Karengro is a gypsy term meaning 'boyplant' it is found in Transylvania and has some similarity to an orchid. It is believed to promote conception and increase sex drive.

Kava Piperaceae and Kava Kava

(Piper methysticum) Kava Piperaceae, sometimes referred to as 'kava kava', is a Polynesian perennial plant related to the pepper found in the South Sea Islands. It has heart-shaped leaves and short spikes that are covered with flowers. Its botanical name, *piper methysticum* was given by the explorer Captain James Cook and literally means 'intoxicating pepper', because it was used for thousands of years to brew an intoxicating alcoholic drink called Kava. This drink is said to be a natural tranquilizer, helps with insomnia and to rouse and heighten sexuality. The Polynesian natives drink kava after wedding ceremonies and are evidently highly stimulated by the drink. Kava drink is made by chewing the root of the pepper plant and spitting it into a kava bowl, the drink is then strained and served in a coconut shell. Kava is mentioned in the *Magical and Ritual Use of Herbs* "as a friend to lovers"; it generates warm emotions, euphoric and loving feeling, resulting in it being used as a supplement for depression. Kava is also reputed to aid tranquil sleep and sometimes to cause vivid, erotic and exotic dreams. Kava has been used in rituals of Tantric yoga and is said to initiate blissfull feelings.

213

Kidneys
The kidneys of some fowl, sheep, pigs and cattle are believed to stimulate sexual functions and are often used in amatory dishes.

King's Crow
In Malaya a charm and love philtre is made with the bile of a bird called the King's Crow.

Kite
In Hindu ancient erotic literature, to consummate sexual domination, a prescription often used required a mixture of honey and cowach, the prickly hairs of a tropical pod, alongside the remains of a dead kite, in pulverised form.

Koribó
(Tanaecium noctumum) This liana thrives in the tropical and coastal zones of South America and Central America. The delicate flowers are closed during the day, only opening at dusk and give out a sweet intoxicating aroma similar to almonds. The milky sap that flows though the plant can be powdered and ingested during shamanic ceremonies as psychedelic snuff. The Choco Indians revere it as an aphrodisiac; the root cortex is used to make an aphrodisiac tea. The brujas 'witches' of South America use the leaves of this shrub for flying trances and for sexual rituals and cures for impotence.

Kosth
Kosth is a preparation applied to the genitals in the Hindu amatory tradition, comprehensively illustrated in the *Ananga Ranga*. It consists of costus arabicus, lechi, chikana, askhand, and kanher root, gajapimpali, pounded and mixed with butter.

Kuili
According to the Hindu manual *Ananga Ranga* Kuili is used to recover sexual vigour, it was made of kuili powder, Kanta-gokhru, lechi, asparagus racemosus, and cucumber. Mixed with milk the resultant drink is said to be highly strengthening to the sexual urge.

Kyphi
Kyphi was an ancient Egyptian mixture applied to the genitals to stimulate an erection and arouse sexual desire.

Lakshmana

(Calonyction muricatum) Lakshmana is a vine that grows in India with yellow heart shaped leaves and a flower that smells like saffron. The plant is also called the 'Shiva tendril' and is considered a yoga plant and symbolizes the kundalini serpent, which is the active female energy in Tantric yoga. The kundalini when fed awakens the sexual powers in the body; Lakshmana is known to feed the serpent. In mythology the plant is used to brew an elixir of life and is used in Ayurvedic medicine as a restorative and an aphrodisiac.

Lamb

Lambs' testes were recommended by the famous Italian chef, Cartolomeo Scappi as an aphrodisiac aid, they were often considered the prize treat in Arabian feasts.

Lamprey

Lamprey is an eel-like fish and is said to increase the seminal fluid and promote conception and sexual vigour.

Land Cattrops/Puncture vine

(Goksura Tribulus terrestris) A high altitude perennial trailing plant with fruits that contain several seeds, it grows wild all over Africa. Known to be an excellent aphrodisiac for the elderly and over tired. It is also used for urinary disorder, incontinence and impotence.

Lard

Lard mixed with crushed and strained garlic was long used as an erotic ointment.

Laurel Leaves

(Laurus nobilis Linnaeus) Laurel leaves were used in the Orient to promote amatory exercise, they are also widely used in love charms. According to Pliny the Elder, wreaths upon the brows of victors began

215

with Livia Drusilla, the wife of Caesar Augustus. Legend says a gift was dropped in Livia's lap by an eagle. Afterwards the Emperor when taking part a triumph held a laurel branch from the original tree in his hand and wore a wreath of its foliage on his head, and subsequently every one of the ruling Caesars did the same.

Lavender

(Lavandula angustifolia) Ruler Mercury, small doses of lavender are said to cause sexual excitation, and a few flowers in tobacco induce a dream-like state. Lavender essential oil is a good addition to any massage mix. Romans used it for its beautiful fragrance and protective associations, the plant being sacred to the goddess Vesta goddess of the Sacred Fire, who used it to bathe and cleanse their wounds. It was also, revered for its antiseptic quality. Sex-starved Empress Josephine served a chocolate and lavender concoction when her thoughts and attentions turned to sexual delights. Her husband, Napoleon, not always matching her lustful thoughts "not tonight, Josephine" may have been a common cry. For Napoleon too this soon became his favourite nighttime tipple.

Lecithin

Lecithin is a nitrogenous fatty substance that appears in certain foods and is considered an element in inducing sexual desire.

Leeks

(Allium) Like its close relations garlic and onions, leeks have a long reputation as a powerful aphrodisiac.

Lentils

(Garbanzos chana) Lentils were widely used in ancient Greece and were believed to stimulate sexual desire. In the 6th century, chickpeas were believed to be an aphrodisiac; while curiously enough, lentils were considered to have the opposite effect, and this was probably the reason why the lentil was included in the diet in monasteries on meatless days (Van der Maesen, 1972).

Ling-shih

(Ganoderma lucidum) Ling-shih has been known since the Ming dynasty and in Japan it was called the 'mushroom of immortality'. Because of its rarity it is also called the 'phantom mushroom'. There are many legends concerning its magical powers. The mushroom became the sign of the Taoists as a symbol of long, health and sexually fulfilled life. Elixirs of immortality and powerful aphrodisiacs were brewed with it.

Liquorice

(Glycyrrhiza glabra) Ruler Mercury, liquorice or licorice is an herbaceous plant. Its roots are valued in confectionary and medicine. Liquorice is used for a tonic for the adrenal glands, digestive and intestinal problems and has been added to recipes for many aphrodisiacs. Magically liquorice can be used in any love philtre or brew, and also added to incense as it is reputed to incite strong sexual passion. It is also an aromatic ingredient in any smoking mixture. Culpeper recommended liquorice for urinary complaints. The pleasant quality of true licorice led to it being incorporated into many traditional Chinese remedies, where it was credited with harmonizing the body's response. "Liquorice root possesses demulcent properties: and hence is useful to allay coughs, and in catarrhal affections. It has also been found serviceable in irritable conditions of the mucous membrane of the urinary organs, etc."

Lion's fat

According to Sinibaldus lion's fat was a popular medieval aphrodisiac treatment applied to the genitals. The *Geneanthropoeia* is a comprehensive textbook in Latin that is in the nature of a course in sexology and anatomy. The author is Johannes Benedict Sinibaldus, an Italian professor of medicine who published the book in Rome in 1642. Many chapters in the book deal with aphrodisiacs, especially from an historical viewpoint and also contain numerous warnings against excessive amatory activity.

Liqueurs

Many liqueurs, including Chartreuse and Benedictine, have long been held in great esteem as aphrodisiac aids.

Liquids

According to Nefzawi, the author of the erotic manual *The Perfumed Garden* asserts that greasy liquids act as an anti-aphrodisiacal.

Liver

Dried liver was used by the Romans as an ingredient in love potions. Horace, the Roman poet, makes mention of this in one of his Epodes as popular in his days as an aphrodisiac.

Lizard

Lizards were favoured in many Arab countries for their aphrodisiac qualities. An old recipe for potency consists of Chinese cubebs, cloves, cinnamon, Roumi opium, ginger, cardamom, mountain lizard and white pepper. Pounded together and boiled in sweet olive oil. Frankincense can be added and coriander seed, then the entire composition in now macerated and mixed with bee honey. Aelius an Alexandrian physician of the second century A.D. recommended the flesh of lizard to ensure virility. By itself, the lizard is powdered and drunk with sweet wine, acting as an aphrodisiac and providing erotic stimulus. An African animal *lacerta scincus,* an amphibious lizard that was commonly used ground to a powder as a very powerful aphrodisiac. Lizards were brought by Egyptian fellahin to Cairo, then shipped to the Mediterranean ports, particularly Marseilles and Venice where they were much sought after as aphrodisiacs.

Lobster

Lobster and crayfish are considered aphrodisiacs for their delicate seafood taste.

Loha-Bhasma

(Yogaraj-guggulu)

Loha-Bhasma is a preparation of ferrous oxide, used in India as Ayurvedic preparation and an aphrodisiac.

Lotus, Sacred Lotus

(Nelumbo nucifera) The lotus flower grows like a water lily in still waters, ponds and gardens. The lotus flower has been praised in countless religious hymns, it is considered to be the birth place of the gods, viewed as a symbol of enlightenment, eternal life and spiritual development. The white lotus is the sacred lotus, the red is found in ponds throughout India. It is said that lotus flowers sprang up from the ground in the foot steps of the

Buddha. It has long been used as a medicine, healing food and aphrodisiac. The blossom is a symbol of the cosmic vagina, the seeds a symbol of divine creation. The seeds are used as an aphrodisiac. The Hindu Goddess Lakshmi is depicted standing on a lotus leaf.

Love Potions and Love Charms

Such devices have always been popular particularly in the Orient, in India women use a variety of charms and amulets to inspire to or retain passion in their lovers. In his *Anatomy of Melancholy*, Robert Burton, the 17th century chronicler, has this to say of aphrodisiacs. "The last battering engines are philtres, amulets, charms, images and such unlawful means. If they cannot regale of themselves by the help of bawds, panders, and their adherents, they will fly for succour to the devil himself. I know there be those that denye the devil can do any such thing, and that there is no other fascination than that which comes by the eyes."

It was given out, of old, that a Thessalian wench had bewitched King Philip to dote on her, and by philtres enforced his love, but when Olympia, his queen saw the maid was of an excellent beauty well brought up and qualified, these, quoth she, were the philtres which enveagled King Philip.

Lovage

(Levisticum officinale) Ruler the Sun. Lovage originates in Southwest Asia but now grown in many gardens both the herbage and the root have been considered aphrodisiacs. The fresh root is used to prepare a love drink that is said to soften even the most strait-laced girls. The plant is considered the 'rod of love', a symbol of love with an unambiguous male component. Culpeper's herbal recommends lovage for warming the lower stomach and groin and for easing the bowels

Lozenges

Anciently, lozenges and pastilles, often perfumed with ambergris, were on sale as aphrodisiac aids in Greece. They were called appropriately, avunculae Cypriae, the Aunts of the Cyprian goddess Venus.

Lychee

(Litchi chinensis Sonn. Sapindaceae) Lychee is said to be aphrodisiac for males if they skin the fruit, gently extract the stone and then inserts the tip of his tongue in the crevice that remains.

Lycopodium
(Lycopodium Clavatum (Lyc)
Lycopodium was a plant with a claw-like root, once believed to have aphrodisiac properties. Often used in homeopathic medicine as a mood regulator.

Lysergic Acid, Diethyl-Amide, Adrenochrome.
These drugs have similar properties and actions to mescaline and produce hallucinations and may have erotic function, but they are all highly dangerous and should not be taken without medical supervision.

Maca
(Lepidium meyenii) Maca is a root vegetable, related to the potato, which is grown in the high central Peruvian Andes. Its tubers contain a number of steroid glycosides with oestrogen like actions. Dried, powdered maca is used to increase energy and stamina and has a reputed aphrodisiac effect for men and women and can aid female fertility and male impotence.

According to Peruvian history, during the height of their empire, Incan warriors would devour maca before entering into battle. The maca would imbue them with a fierce strength and made the Inca into a daunting adversary; but after entering the conquered city the Incan soldiers were forbidden from eating maca, to protect the native women from the powerful sexual impulses of the invading force; the dried root was also used as a currency by the Inca. Maca is also used for stress and depression; it is a mood enhancer that also works as an aphrodisiac, and fertility enhancer; but too much of the herb acts as a laxative, probably because of its high fibre content.

The Spanish invaders were very impressed with maca and used it to build up their horses when they saw the effect it had in the local native communities. The Inca considered maca as a gift from the gods, along

220

with potatoes and corn and it was used by shamans in their medicine rites.

Mackerel

As is the case with many species of fish, mackerel is believed to stimulate sexual desire.

Maerua Arenaria

(Hybanthus enneaspermus (Linn.) Maerua arenaria is an herb native to India, which is widely used to promote desire and sexual vigour.

Magic

Many herbs, artefacts and crystals have been used in magical charms and spells to attract a sexual partner or to enhance, stimulate and prolong the sexual act. This is true in all cultures of the world and the Middle Ages, among occult practitioners there were a kind of standardized and acknowledged pharmacopoeias whose aim was the furtherance of erotic capacity. In the late 17th century concoctions, intended for aphrodisiac purposes and involving scatological ingredients, was officially endorsed by the University Faculty of Leipzig, in Germany.

Magic Mushrooms

(Stropharia cubensis) This mushroom was used by Mexican shaman and sorcerers, who referred to it as 'the flesh of the gods,' in order to have visions and heal the sick. It often produces erotic visions and sensations, even an orgasm, while in a trance. In low doses it makes an excellent aphrodisiac by heightening erotic feeling.

Mallows

(Althea officinalis (MarshMallow) Ruler Venus. The root of the mallow in goat's milk is said to excite the sexual urge, according to Pliny the Elder, the Roman encyclopaedist. In contrast, if the root was eaten dry it was believed to act as anti-aphrodisiac. The sap of mallow, together with three mallow roots tied together aroused the passions of woman, according to the same writer. Pliny believed that Mallows would cure all the diseases of man. The ancient Celts believed that placing the disk-shaped fruit over a dead (holy) man's eyes would keep evil spirits from entering the body in an attempt to get into heaven. According to the

doctrine of signatures the hairs on the plant meant that it would help to grow hair and stimulate sexual desire.

Mandrake

(Atropa mandragors, Mandragora officinarrum) This plant is sometimes called Mandragora, and belongs to the potato family. It has dark leaves, with purple flowers, and a tomato like fruit; it is indigenous to the Mediterranean area and Palestine. The Hebrew name for mandrakes is Dudaim, from the root dud meaning love. Pharmaceutically tested in recent times, mandrake shows aphrodisiac properties. The yellow fruit of the mandrake, of the size of a large plum emits a peculiar but characteristic odour.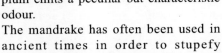
The mandrake has often been used in ancient times in order to stupefy criminals who had been sentenced to crucifixion. In the 5th century A.D. Theodoric, king of the Ostrogoths used mandrake in a wine decoction when preparing victims for crucifixion.

The Greek satirist Lucian also alludes to the dulling effect of the mandrake potion. The Greeks called it love apples and bestowed the name of Mandragoritis upon Venus. The mandrake is one of the examples of plants and herbs that resemble the human genitalia and thus has been associated with aphrodisiac qualities. In Roman time it was often used in love charms and love philtres. The ancient Homeric witch Circe used infusions of it in her magic brews, hence the root was also known as 'the plant of Circe'. Speaking of the plant, Pliny the Elder, says: "the whole variety of Eryngium know to resemble the male organ in shape will excite a woman to love." legend has it that Phaon, the Lesbian, was so passionately loved of Sappho because of a charm made from mandrake. Issac Vossius, a 17th century scholar, states "it is believed that in the mandrake lies the power of acquiring love." In Persia, the mandrake was used to secure a husband's love.

In the 18th century Chinese Mandragora was the name for ginseng. A mandragorite was a term applied to one addicted to mandrake as a narcotic. John Gerarde, author of *The Herball or General Histories of Plantes*, published in 1633, speaks of the beneficial effect of the plant on barren women. The notion of the efficiency of love powders as also prevalent in the 15th century in England that in the Parliament summoned by King Richard 11, on his usurping the throne, it was publicly urged as a charge against Lady Grey that she had bewitched King Edward 1V by strange potions and amorous charms. Shakespeare used the expression in this sense in *Othello*.

> Not poppy, nor mandragora,
> Nor all the drowsy syrups of the world
> Shall ever medicine thee to that sweet sleep
> Which thou owd'st yesterday.

Mandrake is also mentioned as a soporific in Shakespeare's *Anthony and Cleopatra*, the queen said:

> Give me to drink mandragora
> That I might sleep out this great gap of time
> My Anthony is away.

It was also administered by the ancient Greeks to surgical patients and in the Middle Ages it was similarly recommended in the 11th century by philosopher and physician Avicenna for use during surgery or chronic disease. Dioscorides, a Greek physician who served in the army of the Emperor Nero, calls mandrake circaea, the plant of Circe, because its root was thought to be a very effective love philtre. He also refers to a wine concoction of mandrake root that was used in surgical operations. The concoction was also used in the preparation of philtres.

Many legends associated with the mandrake are incorporated in a novel entitled *Vampire*, by Hans Heinz-Ewers.

In folklore, the eating of mandrake is also considered an aid to conception, in the Middle Ages mandrake was regularly used in magic rites and sorcery. A 17th century traveller says that the eating of mandrake helps conception. The Greeks used the root, to excite passion; hence the association with the Goddess Aphrodite who was known as Mandragoritis, 'She of the Mandrake'. In some folklore there are considered to be Mandrakes and Womandrakes, the former being white, the latter black. Mandrake has been described as 'drowsy syrup.'

223

In contemporary Greece the amatory properties of mandrake are still known, even late 19th century the young men of Athens carried pieces of mandrake with them in their satchels as love charms. In Italy the comedy Mandragola was based on the power of the mandrake to make woman fruitful and Sir James G Frazer, in his Folk Lore in the Old Testament, said that orthodox Jews in America Imported mandrake from the Orient to help a barren wife to conceive.

La Fontaine, the French fabulist, had a tale, *La Mandragora*, dealing with the erotic impact of the root. The Arabs call it 'face of an idol' or 'man-plant'. The Greek biographer Plutarch called the plant 'man-likeness,' because is often resembles the human form and sometimes the shape of the male member. The Roman encyclopaedist, Pliny the Elder says "it is said to bear a marked likeness to the genitals of either sex; it is rarely met with, but if a root resembling the male organ of the human species is found by a man, it will ensure him woman's love," Columella, a Roman poet, also called mandrake 'semi-human'.

In Germany it was called the 'little Gallows Man'. This term is associated with the folk tradition that mandrakes sprang up in ground near which a criminal had been hanged on a gallows. Columella the Roman bucolic poet from the 1st century A.D. called mandrake vesanus, 'maddening', because it was in his time believed to form a component in love potions that were intended to drive the victim mad with desire. John Wierus the 16th century demonographer exposes the procedure in the monumental monograph on witchcraft, *De Praestigiis Daemonum et incantationibus ac Veneficiis*. He said; "Impostors carve these plants while still green they make and female forms, insert millet or barley seeds in such parts as they desire the likeness of human hair to grow."

Mango

The name 'mango' is derived from the Tamil word 'mangkay' or 'man-gay' and known as the 'food of the gods'. As long as 4,000 years ago. When the Portuguese traders settled in Western India they adopted the name as 'manga'. The Mango tree plays a sanctified role in India; it is a symbol of love and some believe that the Mango tree can grant wishes. In the Hindu culture hanging fresh mango leaves outside the front door during Ponggol (Hindu New Year) and Deepavali is considered a blessing to the house. Mango leaves are used at weddings to ensure the couple conceive plenty of children. In India the mango is believed to boost sex drive and prolong love making and is featured prominently in Hindu erotology. The following recipe is found in Hindu literature: Arris root, dressed with oil of mango. Placed for six months in a hole in the trunk of the sisu tree, then taken out, made into an ointment and applied to the genitalia.

Marigold

(European Calendula) Ruler Sun, magically speaking, bathing in marigold infusion is said to infuse our aura with the power to attract the opposite sex. Marigold is good for the heart, raises spirits and increases sexual stamina. Throughout the Middle Ages and the Elizabethan era and for centuries afterwards, certain herbs were considered to have not only particular healing powers but often magic powers as well. Is it reasonable to think that someone would purchase a soap ball because it contained herbs believed to be an aphrodisiac or which warded off the evil eye?

Marijuana

This drug cannabis sativa is a decided aphrodisiac. Its use can be dangerous, both psychically and organically. (See Cannabis and Hemp)

Marjoram

(Origamum Majorana) Ruler Mercury, Marjoram is an aromatic herb often used in cookery and for flavouring foods. Among the Romans marjoram was known to have an aphrodisiac value. Sweet marjoram essential oil can be used in massage oil mixes to enhance sleep and relaxation. Culpeper recommends it for after childbirth to encourage regular periods and for women who have lost interest in sex.

Marking Nut

(Bhallataka Somecarpus Anacardium)

The marking nut is a tree that grows in the forests of eastern India; it has seeds that are black in colour when ripe. The outer shell of the seed is removed and a cashew-like pulp appears which is eaten, but it can cause an allergic reaction for some.

The marking nut is used as an aphrodisiac to strengthen the male genital organ and in dysmenorrhoea.

Marrow

According to tradition bone marrow is a source of vitality, thus a paté of marrow was a common concoction for heightening sexual appetite. The Roman poet Horace refers to dried marrow as a reliable aphrodisiac.

Marzipan
It is said that a slice of marzipan followed by a drink of hippocras is an amatory prescription, advised by Rabelais in his *Gargantua* and *Pantagruel*.

Mastic
(Paederia foetidia) Mastic is an Arab aphrodisiac, it is a drink made from the fruit of the Mastic tree, pounded with honey and oil, and it was recommended for increasing the sperm count.

Matico
(Piper angustifolium) This pepper plant grows in the tropical regions of the Americas. The Indians of Central and South America used them as a spice, in pre-Columbian times the leaves were used to treat wounds, the fruit and leaves were used as an aphrodisiac.

Matwu
(Cacalia cordifolia) A shrub native to the Americas it has heart shaped leaves and yellow flowers. It belongs to the so called 'false peyote' plants that are used in ritual in place of peyote; used to treat fatigue and sterility.

May Day Celebrations
May Day and the maypole were the focal point of many traditional spring games and festivities, and are a relic of ancient pagan phallic worship. (See chapter 7)

Meat
In the Hindu religion the eating of meat in prohibited, but meat was believed to increase sexual power and is often mentioned in Hindu sexological manuals. Lean, red meat in particular is credited with powerful aphrodisiac effects.

Melons
In ancient Persia, melons were considered an aphrodisiac and eaten regularly to stimulate the appetite for both food and love. Melon is still commonly served as a starter for seduction meals in many cultures.

Mescaline
(Prosopis) Mescaline is a substance derived from the tufts of a cactus called Peyotl or Lophophora Williamsii or Anholonium Lewinni. The plant grows wild in Central America, Mexico and in Texas. This cactus appears as a cluster of small button like growths, the main root being underground. The small growths when dried are known as Peyotl or mescal buttons. They are bitter and leathery in texture. In Mexican

folklore the use of this drug is well documented. Peyotl was known to the Indians of South America and was also used in Aztec religious rituals. The cactus was called 'flesh of the gods,' and was an object of worship among native Indian priests. The Spaniards who invaded Mexico called the cactus 'Devil Flesh'. In parts of South America the mescal button was harvested in a religious ceremony. Iin some locations stone statues are fashioned in the shape of the buttons and are the object of worship. A similar form of reverence is associated with some mushrooms which also give out a mescaline like substance.

Over time the use of Peyotl was extended throughout South America, Mexico, Central and North America, although the use of the plant was prohibited, the Native Indians continued in their traditional ways, taking the buttons in a mélange. At the end of the 19th century, scientific investigations began to examine the properties of the cactus and its effects on the mind and the body. Some experiments disclosed remarkable visions and hallucinations after taking the mescal infusion. Havelock Ellis in 1902 and Aldous Huxley in 1954 and 1956 experienced the effect of the drug and then described their own personal feelings. Huxley the author did so in his books *The Doors of Perception* and *Heaven and Hell.*

It seems that Peyotl intoxication induces hallucinations and delusions, associated with 'a horror chamber' and that, the more twisted sexual desires, are also intensified. Mescaline is a very dangerous drug and should never be taken without medical supervision.

Milk

Among Arabs washing the genitals in ass's milk was considered a means of stimulating vigour. Poppaea, the wife of the Roman Emperor Nero is said to have bathed in ass's milk for beatifying purposes, Cleopatra was also known to have bathed in ass's milk.

Milk Thistle

(Silybum marianum; Carduus marianus) Milk thistle is a thorny, weed-like plant with purple flowers native to the Mediterranean. Milk thistle seeds contain a powerful mixture of antioxidant bioflavonoid known as silymarin, silymarin can help to improve liver function which may in turn raise testosterone levels and help to improve low sex drive where this is associated with excess alcohol.

Mineral Pitch

(Silajatu) This is an exudate from stones found in mountains. The pitch comes out of stones in the summer season due to exposure to the rays of the sun. Some of these stones can be used as an aphrodisiac and for rejuvenation of the body.

Mineral Waters

Bathing in specified mineral waters has for many centuries been considered an aphrodisiac tool. The procedure was well-known to the ancient Romans who constantly practiced it in resorts throughout the Roman Empire. In Arabic texts dedicated to erotic advice, it is recommended to bathe to increase sexual vigour. Radioactive baths are said to act beneficially in a sexual objective, also arsenical springs, cold water treatments and hydrotherapy.

Mint

Ruler Venus. According to the erotologist Mattioli, mint is a herb that is effective in strengthening male vigour and reputed to have aphrodisiac properties. According to *Culpeper's Herbal* 'it stirreth up venery or bodily lust'.

Mistletoe

(Viscum album) Ruler Sun. Mistletoe is sacred to Heme/Cernunnos, the white berries being associated with the white beads of his semen. It is also sacred to Balder, the Norse god slain with a Mistletoe dart. Alive, Balder is the sun god and master of all vegetation, the green man. At his sacrificial death he becomes god of the underworld and spouse of its queen Hel. The mistletoe is also sacred to the Norse fertility and moon goddess Freya. In magical traditions, from the earliest times, mistletoe has been one of the most magical, mysterious, and sacred plants of European folklore. It was considered a bestower of life and fertility; a protector against poison; and an aphrodisiac. Later, the ritual of cutting the mistletoe from the oak came to symbolize the emasculation of the old King by his successor. Mistletoe was long regarded as both a sexual symbol and the 'soul' of the oak. It was gathered at both mid-summer and mid-winter solstices, and the custom of using mistletoe to decorate houses at Christmas is a survival of the Druid and other pre-Christian traditions. Mistletoe is still ceremonially plucked on mid-summer eve in a number of Celtic and Scandinavian countries. Kissing under the mistletoe is first found linked with the Greek festival of Saturnalia and later with primitive marriage rites. Mistletoe was believed to have the

power of bestowing fertility, and the dung from which the mistletoe was thought to arise was also said to have "life-giving" power. In Scandinavia, mistletoe was considered a plant of peace, under which enemies could declare a truce or fighting spouses kiss and make-up. In certain parts of England the Christmas mistletoe is burned on the twelfth night lest all the boys and girls who have kissed under it never marry. And for those who wish to observe the correct etiquette: a man should pluck a berry when he kisses a woman under the mistletoe, and when the last berry is gone, there should be no more kissing! A true love powder, often used in love magic by ancient witches and wizards.

Moh

(Bassia Latifolia) The Moh tree produces flowers rich in sugar. It was used in India to manufacture a liquor called arrack. The pith of the moh tree pounded mixed with cow's milk was taken as a wholesome drink. The *Ananga-Ranga* is the Hindu compendium of sexology. It recommends this recipe for the renewal of virility.

Mollusca

The mollusca and testaceous animals in particular, have been considered to be of potency for amatory relations.

Moly

(Alliium) Moly is a legendary herb, with white flowers and black roots; it is credited with magical qualities. In Homer, Hermes gives the herb to Ulysses to protect him against the guile of Circe. Frequently it is identified with Allium Molly, wild garlic. John Milton mentions the plant Moly in *Paradise Lost*. It is credited with everything from being an aphrodisiac to preventing the Black Death during the Middle Ages. Tennyson refers to beds of amaranth and moly in *The Lotus Easters*, and the plant was often associated with sexual regeneration. Moly could be a Phoenician term or an Egyptian one used in Greek in a generic sense. It has also been suggested that moly may be equated with *Peganum Harmala*, wild rue, a plant indigenous to Southern Europe and Asia.

Morning Glory

(Ipomoea violacea) Morning glory is a creeper native to the Americas; it thrives in the clear areas of the Central American rain forests. The seeds were used in pre-Columbian times for medicinal and ritual purposes. An ideal aphrodisiac for women and for women's problems, it was consumed at religious festivals. The seeds, which Indian healers

believe to be the home of a god, contain llysergic acid that helps gynaecological and urinary conditions; but over-use of this plant can cause miscarriage and psychedelic effects.

Motherwort

(Leonurus Cardiaca) Ruler Venus. Motherwort probably derives its name from its use as a sedative infusion, taken to ease the pain of childbirth and because it was also taken to prevent miscarriages. The infusion can be taken for many menstrual problems, especially those which may be stress related. Some people recommend this plant to increase male virility and this may help with any sexual problems which are allied to anxiety or stress. Motherwort was recommended by Culpeper as it makes women joyful mothers of children and settles their wombs; therefore they called it motherwort, it can also bring forth a woman's courses. Because of its affinity with Venus, motherwort can also be used in many love spells including pouches, potions and philtres; however it is quite an unpleasant tasting herb, so keep it to a minimum, in potions to take internally. If you add the herb or infusion of your bath water, it is said to draw lovers to you like moths to a flame.

Mouse

According to Pliny the Elder the excrement of a mouse when smeared on the genitals would render that person impotent. Yuck!

Mugwort

(Artemisia vulgaris) Ruler Venus. Mugwort is a slightly different species than Wormwood, but of the same genus (and oils). This water-side plant Mugwort was used in the Orient as an aphrodisiac. It is also recommended by Culpeper for women to bring forth their courses and for treatment after pregnancy and during labour. Use in a bath or as an ointment. The name Artemisia is from the Goddess Artemis (1st century AD) who inspired the plant's genus name.

Muira puama

(Ptychopetalum olacoides; P. guyannna; Liriosma ovata) Muira puama is a small tree found in the Brazilian rainforest, it has white flowers that smell like jasmine. It is widely used by natives of the Amàzon and Orinoco river basins to enhance sexual desire and combat impotence. It has an extremely hard timber, the wood and bark of which is boiled to make an alcoholic drink. Muira puama is also known as 'potency wood' or 'tree of virility' in Brazil and is used as a tonic. Taken as a tea it is used to treat sexual impediment, improve potency and is also claimed to

prevent baldness.

Mushrooms

Raw mushrooms, like truffles, have an odour reminiscent of sex and were widely regarded as aphrodisiacs by the ancient Romans and Greeks; Arabs also consider the eating of mushroom as an aphrodisiac. There are numerous varieties of mushroom that have toxic properties. Two thousand years ago these toxic properties were already common knowledge, in the Middle Ages medicinal texts refer to these characteristics and cases are cited of dried mushrooms mixed with food and wine, being administered to potential victims. In the 16th century an Italian Cardinal, living in Rome, had a preparation made of granules of dried *Amanita Muscaria* and secreted in a ring that he wore on his finger. The poison was thus ready to hand whenever necessary.

Musk

(Kasturi Moschus moschiferus) Musk is a brown, bitter, volatile substance, extracted from a gland near the genitals of the musk deer and of a species of goat indigenous to Tartary. In Persia and Tibet musk is used in food for its amatory properties. The smell of musk is associated with the ideal woman according to the Hindu *Kama Sutra.* Arab writers commented on the effectiveness of perfuming oneself with musk as an aid of enhancement before sexual activity. In Oriental stories musk often appears as an alluring erotic factor in sensual literature. Musk could also be taken internally according to old medical records of the 18th century and would stimulate the male genitals. Musk was in the past often used in perfumes and preparations. Its use is now prohibited in most parts of the world. Musk is a stimulant and aphrodisiac.

Musk Rose

(Rosa Mosqueta) Ruler Venus. Musk Rose is a very special perfume as it acts as a combination of the love powers of Venus and the lustful energies of the Horned God. It is particularly useful in the ritual invocations of Cernummus/Heme and to invoke the powers of the God into his priest as in the ceremony of 'Drawing down the sun'. This perfume is also helpful to those involved in Tantric magic, or in rituals of sex or seduction. Try using just a little to perfume the belly as this is reputed to inflame the senses of your partner. For those who find the energies of pure musk too powerful, or wish to temper lustful longings with love and friendship, musk rose is an ideal substitution being derived from plant material, and not animal like musk.

231

Mustard

(Brassica nigra) Ruler Mars. Since ancient times, both the seeds and the plant have been attributed with effects that are said to promote virility. For this reason monks were forbidden to use mustard. It is often documented that hot mustard baths are recommended as assisting and enhancing the libido of women. Mustard seeds can be made into a strong infusion that was believed to be an effective aphrodisiac.

Mustela Piscis

Some records state that eating the brains of the *Mustela Piscis* is an aphrodisiac for women.

Mutton

Roasted mutton with caraway seeds was often eaten in aphrodisiac meals by Arabs and is still regarded as a sensory delight.

Myrrh

(Commiphora Myrrha) Ruler Jupiter. A composite of eggs boiled with myrrh, pepper and cinnamon, taken on several consecutive days is recommended by many Arabs for strengthening amorous vigour. The gum is especially prized in the Orient and used as a medicinal aid in various illnesses as well as an erotic stimulant. The essential oil of myrrh can also be used in massage for its stimulating effects.

Myrtle

In the Middle Ages, pulverized myrtle leave were applied to the body as a sexual stimulation. A herb used to add to love spells and love baths to keep a love alive and exciting. Every bride should carry some myrtle in her bra when getting married, to insure a long and happy marriage. A putative love tonic was also made from the water in which myrtle leaves and flowers had been steeped. Used in many European countries, according to an old recipe. When the Goddess Aphrodite arose from the waves and realized her nakedness, she plucked some sprigs from a myrtle bush to cover herself. This is why it is said the myrtle plant has leaves shaped like a vagina, the outer lips *(labia majora)* being likened to the leaves of the myrtle, and inner *(labia minora)* to its fruit. Venus too was supposed to have been born from the sea and to have covered her nakedness with myrtle leaves. The Three Graces in attendance on Venus and her son, Cupid, were crowned with Myrtle leaves.

Nail Parings

According to the Ancient Romans, nail parings were used in magic rites for aphrodisiac purposes. Nail pairings and hair have been used throughout the centuries in love charms and spells to attract or control a prospective partner.

Nedde

In some Arab countries a mixture of a mixture of perfumes with benzoin and amber predominating is called nedde. This mixture which is almost black in colour is fashioned into small cylinders and used as an aphrodisiac.

Nepenthes

Nepenthes is a drug or potion frequently mentioned by Homer, especially in the Odyssey, as having the effect of banishing sorrow or mental inhibitions that could obstruct the sexual act. It has been variously identified with opium, hashish and Panax Chironium of Theophrastus, the 3rd century BCE Greek philosopher who wrote some volumes of beneficial plants. Theophrastus asserts that infused in wine this drug was administered as an aphrodisiac. A variant of the drug is called nepenthe. Homer called it, 'the gods' drink'

Nettle

(Urtica dioica) Ruler Mars, the stinging nettle is a perennial plant found worldwide, though few people realize its medicinal effects especially on the urinary system. Since ancient times they have been used for sexual stimulation. Nettle extracts seem to increase testosterone and increase sex drive. In many cultures flagellation with nettles was exercised upon the buttocks and adjacent parts to have a powerful effect upon the organs of generation. This practise was well known in Roman times, medical writer Celsus, mentions it in the 1st century A.D. The Romans had frequently used urtication, beating with

233

nettles, to arouse the sexual appetites and it is mentioned in the roman novelist and satirist's Patronius's work. Nettles are mentioned by Menghus Faventinus, a medical writer, and by Rabelais; they both allude to them in procuring the vigour necessary for sexual stamina; the seeds can also be ingested. Nettle tea is good for the heart, skin, blood and bones as it is high in minerals.

Niando

(Alchomea floribunda) This bushy plant is native to Africa and has been used since ancient times in magic and religious ceremonies. It induces hallucinations and can, if taken as a beverage, invoke blissful feelings and is known as a powerful aphrodisiac.

Nicotine

The nicotine in tobacco has been held to produce an aphrodisiac effect despite such literary condemnation as J. M. Barrie's *My Lady Nicotine.*

Ninjin

Ninjin is a root highly regarded by the Japanese; it has properties that putatively are corresponding to the aphrodisiac virtues of the mandrake root.

Nuoc-Man

Nuoc-Man is an aphrodisiac sauce, consisting of extract of decayed fish, much in use in the Far East, especially among the South Chinese. It contains the two crucial aphrodisiac elements, phosphorus and salt. The sauce is very often spiced with pimento or garlic.

Nutmeg

(Myristica fragrans) Nutmeg is an aromatic seed of a tree native to the East Indies, used to spice food, highly prized in the Orient as an aphrodisiac, especially among Chinese women. Nutmeg contains an amphetamine-like chemical which is harmless in small quantities. If however grated nutmeg is mashed with avocado flesh and chilled overnight, a chemical reaction occurs that is said to produce a pro-sexual effect in men. The nut and the wall are diuretic, lactogogue and also act as a stimulant. It contains an essential oil and the principal component of this oil is myristicin, a substance that also serves as the basis of the 'love drug' MDA, or ecstasy.

Nux Vomica

(Strychnos nux-vomica) This wild tree grows in Asia and has broad leaves, crown like umbels and an orange berry fruit. When dried the seeds are also known as 'poison nuts' or 'crows eyes'. Nux vomica is a

drug that may have stimulating aphrodisiac effects and is effective in cases of impotence, but also causes hallucinations and should never be used without medical supervision. Nux Vomica is also available as a homeopathic remedy.

Nymphaea

Nymphaea is a Hindu aphrodisiac in the form of a compound applied to the body, in oil of hogweed, echites putescens, the sarina plant, yellow amaranth, and the leaf of the mymphaea.

Oats

(Avenal sativa) Ruler the Sun, Oats are a nutritious aphrodisiac that may be taken as porridge or in supplement form. Its reputation as a pro-sexual herb may account for popular saying about 'sowing one's wild oats.' Oats are a wild grass that may have originated in the Middle East and in the Mediterranean basin. Some of the earliest evidence of their use dates to 1000 BCE and is found in cave drawings in northern Europe. Oatmeal and spice cookies have been considered aphrodisiac.

Octopus

The sepia octopus was once in great demand as an aphrodisiac, in the Roman comedy *Casina* by Plautus a scene occurs in which an old man has just been buying some octopus in the market to use as an aphrodisiac.

Olibanum

Olibanum is an aromatic resin often used in medicine, now used as incense. It was known to the Arabs, Greeks and the Romans as an aphrodisiac compound mixed with honey and nutmeg. Olibanum was also known as frankincense and is referred to in The Bible, in the East and the Middle Ages it was prized as a perfume. Among the Turks there was a mixture of olibanum, myrrh, camphor, musk that was a fragrance reputed to stimulate the genitals.

Ololuigui

(Rivea Corynbosa) Ololuigui was a mixture related to mescaline.

Ololiuqui

(Turbina corymbosa) The Ololiuqui is a woody vine that grows in the Americas, the seeds of which are used for religious and medicinal purposes. The plant has psychedelic effects and is considered one of the 'plants of the gods'. Shamans used the plant to visit the astral plane and meet with figures from past and future. It is used in religious ceremonies for prophecy, healing and for its aphrodisiac properties.

Onions

Ruler Mars. Like their relations garlic, onions are reputed to be a powerful aphrodisiac and celibate ancient Egyptian priests were forbidden to eat them. Ovid advised, in his *Remedy for Love*, "that eating onions stirred the passions" and onion soup is recommended in France as a restorative to relight the fires of desire after a fatiguing first wedding night. Martial the Roman epigrammatist, advised, "If your wife is old and your member is exhausted, eat onions a plenty," another poet Columella declared, "That onion inflame and the animate the girls." Greek physician Galen related that pounded onion seed, mixed with honey and taken while fasting had aphrodisiac qualities. There is an old Eastern European recipe that was a supposedly very potent aphrodisiac; it consisted of cooked onions in a salad, mixed with oil, pepper, seasoning and vinegar. Many Oriental dishes intended as aphrodisiacs contained onions. Onions, spices and egg yolk was a popular Arab dish. Onion seed is suggested by Nefzawi in *The Perfumed Garden* as a stimulant; pound the onion seed, sift it mix it with honey and stir the mixture well. Take this mixture while fasting.

Opium

(Papaver somniferum) Opium is extracted from the poppy and has been used throughout history. The poppy from which the opium is extracted was cultivated as a garden flower for thousands of years, the name in Latin means 'sleep producing poppy'. In ancient Sumeria, opium was known as the 'plant of joy'. It was known in the Age of the Pharaohs and throughout Biblical times. King David, who was subject to fits of depression, was cured of his condition by means of a liquid remedy of

which the chief ingredient was reputed to be opium. It was described by Dioscorides who flourished in the 1st century AD. In the Middle Ages it was used for medicinal purposes and also for eating and smoking. Later it acquired an acknowledged aphrodisiac significance. It was used among Turkish soldiers who knew it as amisiam and Portuguese sailors and explorers of the Middle Ages were also familiar with the drug. Hippocrates the Greek physician in the 5th century B.C. knew of poppy juice and Virgil, the Roman epic poet, refers to it as 'the sleep giving poppy'. Theophrastus refers to opium medicinally.

In the 1st century A.D. opium was known as a medicine and is mentioned by Pliny the Elder and Cornelius Nepos, a Roman biographer of the 1st century also alludes to the plant in this respect. Opium was largely used by the Chinese as a sexual provocation both by men and women; but it is has very dangerous side effects. Dr Venette declared opium to be an aphrodisiac, but he also gave warning on its use. Thomas De Quincey, the English essayist, was an opium addict for some 25 years. In his *Confessions of an English Opium Eater*, he describes how he was first introduced to the drug as a remedy for toothache. The Hindu name for opium is *'chandu'*, it is both eaten and smoked and is said to increase vitality and it was often used by the elderly for pain relief. It is mentioned by the Greek poet Homer in his *Iliad*;

> Down sank his head, as in a garden sinks
> A ripened poppy charged what vernal rains;
> So sank his head beneath his helmet's weight.

Vespucci, the traveller and geographer mentions opium as part of a cargo that was brought from India to Lisbon in 1501. The Dutch traveller Linschoten mentions it in his account of voyages in 1596, *Discourse of Voyages into Ye Easte and West Indies*. In Old Egypt the seeds of the white poppy were mixed with flour and honey and made into a cake. The imperial physician at the court of the emperor Nero used potions compounded with opium for sexual problems.

English medicine received its first experimentation with opium in the Middle Ages. From Venice via Germany, it journeyed from Asia Minor in about the 15th century it travelled across India to Macedonia and Persia and began to be cultivated in the 18th century. Laudanum, a by-product of opium, was the name given to a secret remedy concocted by

237

the occultist Paracelsus, in the 16th Century; the legend runs that he carried opium in the hilt of his sword. Morphine is another derivative of opium. Opium and its derivatives are all habit forming drugs, dangerous to take and fatal in the final effect. Opium removes inhibitions, enhances feelings and lessens the sense of responsibility, the aphrodisiac effect is due to the increase of excitement; but for men it does not enhance performance.

Orchid

Orchid means testes in Greek, this plant whose shape has symbolic similarity to the male genitalia? It has had a false reputation as an aphrodisiac.

Orchis and Orchis Hircina

(Orchis morio) Ruler Venus, Orchis morio is a plant of the *Satyrion* species, used in Turkey as a stimulant, it is grown on the mountains near Istanbul. The root of *orchis hircina* was used in ancient times as the basis of a powerful aphrodisiac called Satyrion. The orchis are small orchids that grow in meadows; they were harvested during magical rituals and prepared with a number of other ingredients as beverages or spiced foods. Used in Ayurvedic medicine and by health practitioners in ancient Greece as a tonic and sexual stimulant; it was viewed as a wondrous agent of love.

Oysters

Oysters are probably the most famous aphrodisiac food of all time. They were especially popular in Edwardian times, for they were extremely cheap as was champagne, the drink they are undoubtedly best with. Raw oysters owe their aphrodisiac reputation to their salty, marine odour, their plump resemblance to the female genitalia and their high zinc content; men lose zinc when they ejaculate. Oysters have been mentioned by Emile Zola and the Roman poet Ausonius, and the Roman satirist Juvenal as having aphrodisiac qualities. Their aphrodisiac properties have not been proven but they are sexy to eat.

238

Paprika

(Capiscum annuum) Hungarian red pepper often used as a condiment in food, paprika is reputed to be strongly aphrodisiac.

Papyrus

Many nostrums and traditional medicaments are mentioned throughout Greek literature as aphrodisiac stimulants. Papyri are also extant in which advice is given regarding ithyphallic competence. One such papyrus, rich in detail, is preserved in the Louvre in Paris.

Parsley

(Apium Petroselinum) Ruler Mercury, this was sometimes called 'petersilie' in the Middle Ages, and is used for garnishing foods; also traditionally considered an effective aid in aphrodisiac meals. Parsley has always been a favourite garden plant and in ancient times it was considered a symbol of rebirth. The root was mixed into witches' flying ointments intended to induce erotic ecstasy, it is also used in sachets to attract love. Mix parsley with jasmine and carry in your shoe to make you more attractive to the opposite sex.

Partridge

Many formulae for love potions may be found in the work of Albertus Magnus, who among other things, particularly recommends "The brain of a partridge calcined into powder and swallowed in red wine." A remedy which is also much insisted upon by Platina, who in praising the flesh of the partridge, says; 'the flesh of the partridge strengthens the brain and arouses desire for sexual pleasures'. The flesh of the partridge which is easy to digest strengthens the brain and facilitates conception and sexual arousal. The author of *De Valetudine Tuenda*, on Preserving Health, was an extoller of the flesh of partridge as an aphrodisiac.

Passionflower fruit

(Passiflora incarnate) The passion vine is named for biblical reasons due to its complex flower structure, the five sepals alternating with five petals are said to symbolize the crucifixion, the inner corona of filaments represent the crown of thorns and the styles depict the cross and nails. Nevertheless, the passion fruit is commonly regarded as an aphrodisiac but passionflower tea is better used as a cure for insomnia and relaxant to calm the nerves. Passionflowers are often used in love magic and love charms.

Pastry

Pastry with honey, ginger, syrup of vinegar, nutmeg and many other herbs and spices wa kneaded into breads and pastries intended for sensual meals.

Patchouli

Also known as a love herb; mix with rose petals, orange flowers and orris root for a special love bath. Patchouli was a popular oil used during the hippy movement, and 'free love' of the 1960's.

Pausinystalia yohimbe

(see yohimbe)

Peaches

Ruler Venus. The luscious juicy peach has a shape suggestive of young maidens' buttocks and was highly regarded in ancient China as an aphrodisiac that increased the frequency of sexual intercourse. A peach is the ideal gift to a potential lover; some believe it was a peach not an apple that tempted Adam in the Garden of Eden.

Peanuts

Peanuts contain histidine, an amino acid that can trigger and intensify the orgasm, but beware many people have an allergic reaction to peanuts.

Pearls

Precious stone were always associated with magic properties and to ward off various evil spirits, but also for aphrodisiac intent. There was a legend that Cleopatra was accustomed to dissolve pearls in vinegar and drink the fluid in order to provoke her lustful feelings.

Peas

According to Nefzawi, writer of the Perfumed Garden, peas can create passion; Green peas boiled with onions, powdered with cinnamon ginger, and cardamoms well pounded, would incite the senses.

Pepper

(Piper Nigrum) Genuine or black pepper is a climbing liana found only in the tropics. Both Asian and European folk medicinal traditions consider pepper a superior aphrodisiac. Pepper compounded with nettle seed, this preparation was credited with exciting sexual impulses, White, black and red pepper are all considered to have aphrodisiacal properties.

Perfume

Dr Auguste Galopin was author of *Le Parfum de la Femme et Le Sens Olfactif dans l'Amor* and he made a particular study of the aphrodisiac properties of perfume.

Perch

Most fish are considered as aphrodisiacs; but in the head of the perch there are small stones that are used by witches in preparing love philtres.

Pesoluta

Pesoluta is a plant called by the Romans encyclopaedist Pliny the Elder pesoluta and was said to cause impotence.

Peyote

(Lophophora Williamsii) Peyote or peyoti is a round spineless cactus native to the deserts of Mexico. Peyote produces tiny seeds in round buttons. These mescal buttons have played a religious role since pre-Columbian times. They are consumed ritually in order to evoke visions. The peyote has become a sacrament of the Native American religions. In small doses is has an aphrodisiac effect but can cause strong psychedelic effects.

Pfaffia

(Pfaffia paniculata; P. stenophylia) Pfaffia also known as 'suma', 'Brazilian ginseng' and 'Brazilian carrots', is a ground covering vine found growing in Brazilian forests. It is regarded as a panacea for all ills, by the Xingu tribesmen who call it para todo 'for everything'. It has been used as a female aphrodisiac for at least 300 years and is also used to help treat male impotence.

Pheasant

Pheasant is reputed to have a highly aphrodisiac effect; as is most game.

Pheromones

Pheromones are natural chemical scents the body produces in order to attract others. They are well documented in the animal kingdom as the force that controls all social behavior, including mating. Scientists are now finding that human behavior is also heavily influenced by these invisible social magnets.

Phosphorus

Many believe that foods containing this element are considered of aphrodisiac merit, phosphorus has long been considered a powerful stimulant. It act upon the generative organism, it is recorded in a manner to cause the most violent priapisms. Two French physicians in the 18th century named Leroy and Batattz tried the effect of phosphorus on themselves with helpful aphrodisiac effect. The administration of phosphorus however, even in small doses, has been productive on the other hand of the most horrible and even fatal results. A drake belonging to a chemist having drunk water containing phosphorus continued its amorous activities until it eventually died.

Pillow Books

Pillow books are little books on sexual ideas that were kept in the traditional Japanese lacquered wooden pillows. They were exchanged as gifts between lovers.

Pimento

(Pimenta dioica) This evergreen tree grows in the Caribbean and Central America and the pimento has long been used as a spice. They were said to bring the sexual fire of sexual desire to a glow; in 1132 Peter the Venerable forbade the monks of Cluny to use it on account of its aphrodisiac effect. When pimento and pepper are boiled together with a species of mallow, the resultant compound is applied to rice flour poultices, which in turn are placed in contact with the genitals. This is a Chinese medicine that is highly hazardous, but is often used externally as a stimulant.

Pineapple

(Ananas comosus) Pineapple is one of the many fruits to be considered as an aphrodisiac. Now grown worldwide, but originally from South America, the pineapple has for centuries been used in medicine. It is an excellent diuretic. It is also considered an aphrodisiac. Unripe fruits can cause pregnant women to miscarry.

Pine

(Pinus) Ruler Mars, Pine is sacred to the Horned God and all other gods of the wildwood including Woden, Pan, Sylvanus, Diana and Artemis and is especially sacred to Guede in the voodoo pantheon. The pine cone is a potent fertility symbol, and especially when a pine cone is used to top a ritual wand its phallic symbolism can easily be seen. Pine needles are often used in love charms and sachets.

Pine kernels

The Romans considered pine nuts to have powerful aphrodisiac properties. Together with basil and garlic they make pesto sauce, an ideal gourmet dish for lovers. In the Orient pine seeds were used and greatly prized as a useful aphrodisiac.

Pistachio

(Pistacia vera) Pistachio is a nut that is frequently mentioned in Arab erotic manuals and is said to have an aphrodisiac value. Try dates stuffed with pistachio nuts. Not only are they delicious but they have the look of the female genitals; many, especially in Arabia; swear by them as an aphrodisiac.

Pisteriona

Pisteriona was also called Hierobota, Albertus Magnus, of *De Secretis Milierum*, states that it increases sexual desire. The virtues of the plant are so potent that it is said that the mere possession is a stimulant.

Pitahaya

(Hylocereus triangularis) Also known as Yellow Dragon fruit, native to Jamaica and Cuba. The Pitahaya has an ovoid shape and thick yellow skin with excrescences and bulges that end with a spine. It contains a transparent white flesh that contains a multitude of small edible black seeds. It is  said to be very refreshing and invigorating. "The pitahaya tastes like a kiss blended of love and desire" Andre Breton.

Pizza Urgurdu

In Italy a plant called Pizza urgurdu is said to excite powerful erotic feelings even in the most frigid women; it has also been call the 'Greek Vorax'.

Plaice

As with most fish plaice has an aphrodisiac effect.

Plovers' Eggs

Eggs stuffed with spices were called 'Plovers' eggs' a la Du Barry and had the reputation of being an amatory stimulant.

Polignonia

Polignonia also known as 'Corrigiola' or 'Alchone' is a herb whose juice is reputed to be a potent aphrodisiac according to Albertus Magnus in his *De Secretis Mulierun*.

Pomegranate

(Punica granatum) The pomegranate is a small tree originally from Southwest Asia, but is now grown all over the Mediterranean; it is often called the 'apple of love'. It was venerated as a symbol of Astarte/Aphrodite/Venus; various aspects of the goddess of love, as a result the fruit was said to have strong aphrodisiac effects. The pomegranate is believed by some to be the fruit that tempted Eve in the Garden of Eden, rather than the apple. The *Kama Sutra* recommends splitting the blushing golden globe in two and sharing it for a night of incomparable passion and boosted fertility. According to Pliny the Elder the pith of the pomegranate tree was a sexual stimulant.

Poppy

(Papaver somniferum) Ruler Moon. The opium poppy is now found worldwide and has many different coloured flowers, the petals only last a few days. The capsule opens and the small grey or black seeds fall out. In the past the poppy was consecrated to the gods. It has become enormously important because of opium, which is obtained from the think milky sap extracted from the seed pod. This was used as a medicine, inebriate and aphrodisiac. Poppy seeds are used on bread and as a tasty topping for deserts and cereals.

Potato

The potato does not have any value as a love aid but in the 17th century it was frequently mentioned in this way in Elizabethan dramas. In Shakespeare's *The Merry Wives of Windsor* allusion is made to the sweet potato; 'Let the sky rain potatoes' and again, 'How the devil luxury with his fat rump and potato finger tickles these together.' The reference is to lechery and lust so motivated.

Potions

Lady Jane Gray was accused of bewitching Kind Edward VI of England by way of weird potions and amatory charms.

Prawns

Prawns have always been known as an aphrodisiac and were applauded in epigram by the Greek poet Asclepiades,'For a meal with a courtesan a purchase is to be made at the market of three large and ten small fish and twenty four prawns'.

Prickly Ash Bark

(Zanthoxylum americanum) Prickly ash bark is traditionally used to increase circulation especially in the lower half of the body, very useful if you sit for long periods each day. It is also known to help with sexual potency.

Prickly Poppy

(Argemone Mexicana) This member of the poppy family is native to Mexico and has yellow flowers. The narcotic sap is called 'chicalote opium'. Used by the Aztecs and native healers the dried leaves and flowers are smoked as an aphrodisiac.

Provincia

Provincia is a herb called by the Chaldeans 'Iteri', that when used in foods acts as an aphrodisiac on both men and women, according to Albertus Magnus. It was considered during the Middle Ages to be the most powerful of herbs to induce feelings of love and was identified with the Greek Vorax.

Prunes

Prunes were served in medieval brothels to encourage sex drive in both customers and the exhausted good time girls.

Puff Ball

(Elaphomyces cervinus) The puff ball is a fungus that gets its name from the greyish violet powder it produces, it is also known as 'hart's truffle'. Since ancient times this has been considered an aphrodisiac for both humans and animals, it has been actively rooted out by rutting stags. The fungus was also mixed with feed and given to livestock and acts as a sexual stimulant. For this reason it was used as an aphrodisiac in folk medicines; but they are toxic and have very dangerous side effects.

Purslane or purslaine

Ruler the Moon. Purslane is a succulent herb often found near water, it is used in salads. Purslane is a cooling herb and is believed to act as an anti-aphrodisiac.

Putrajivaka

(Putranjiva roxburghii) Putrajivaka is an evergreen tree found in India and Sri Lanka; it has male and female flowers in rounded clusters. The plant, which is fragrant, cooling and pungent, is an aphrodisiac. It can be used as a laxative and diuretic and for colds and fevers.

Qat

(Catha edulis)

The qat bush grown wild in Northeast Africa, Arabia and the Nile Valley. It was well known to the Ancient Egyptians, who considered it a divine plant. Qat is used fresh; it can be chewed, made into sweets with honey or mixed into beverages like coffee. The dried leaves can be smoked alone or blended with hashish. The effects are said to include mystical insights, and trances as well as being an aphrodisiac.

Quince Tree and Quince Jelly

Ruler Saturn. Quince jelly is said to have an erotic effect on the sensibilities.

Quebracho

(Aspidosperma quebrachoblanco) This yellow blossomed tree grows in the tropical grasslands. Its bark is used in medicine and as an aphrodisiac. It is made into a beer that has contraceptive and abortive properties.

Quinine

(Garrya) Quinine taken in the evening is considered by the Persians as an aphrodisiacal aid.

Quinto Rojo

A notorious herb from Mexico, used in love baths. It is believed to make men's heads turn and make their nature run wild. Only use when sex is desired and with caution. It is used by Mexican prostitutes.

Radishes

Ruler Mars. Radishes, beans, peas and lentils were once popular in Germany as love aids. Radishes were in much demand and were recorded in the poem *Raporum Encomium, the Eulogy of Radishes*, published in Latin in 1549 Lyons by Claude Bigothier. Radishes mixed with honey were made into a potion that was commonly used by the Egyptians in the 5th century B.C.E. Radishes also have a reputation in many Eastern European countries as an aphrodisiac, eaten raw in a dish with boiled cabbage.

Radix Chinae

The radix chinae is a plant to which aphrodisiac qualities have been credited in the medieval and ancient times.

Rakta-Bol

This was the Hindu name for myrrh; powdered rakta-bol, costus arabicus, manishil, borax and aniseed are mixed in oil of sesame. The resultant ointment is then applied to the penis for its stimulatory effect.

Rauwiloid

(Rauwolfia Serpentina) Rauwiloid also known as 'reserpine' and is a drug used to reduce high blood pressure; it also produces erotic dreams with various aphrodisiac effects. The drug is extracted from the dried root of the plant and has been used in India for thousands of years as a medication frequently for headaches and circulation problems. In Sanskrit the plant is known as *sarpagandha*, which means insanity cure. The plant was named after Leonhard Rauwolf, a 16th century German horticulturist and *Serpentina* refers to the snaky roots of the plant. Rauwiloid also grows in the Philippines, China, Java and South and Central America. In Guatemala it is known locally as Chalchapa.

Ray

It is claimed that eating the fish ray can increase seminal fluid in men, and aid fertility.

Red Clover

(Trifolium pratense) Red clover, also known as 'cow clover', 'beebread', 'purple clover' and 'trefoil', is native to Europe and Asia. It is used to balance oestrogen levels and treating menstrual problems. It can benefit women with a low sex drive.

Red Ginseng

(See Ginseng) (Panax Ginseng)

Reishi

(Ganoderma lucidum; Ganoderma japonicum) Reishi is one of seven different varieties of Ganoderma mushrooms each with differing colours. Reishi is red and is regarded as the superior. The Japanese refer to it as Reishi, meaning spiritual mushroom while the Chinese call it ling zhi the mushroom of immortality, and classify it as a superior herb equal to ginseng. Reishi mushrooms help to bring the body's natural functions back to peak performance, including a low sex drive.

Reptiles

Reptiles of many kinds have been considered as aphrodisiacs. They have been eaten, rubbed on the body and used in love magic.

Resin

The Ancient Greeks used all kinds of resin as an aphrodisiac ingredient.

Rhino Horn

Many people particularly in the east believe that rhino horn is an aphrodisiac; there is no scientific proof of this. A man would have more benefit from strapping on the horn than in using it medicinally. The belief derives from the pagan rituals of the horn being a totem of male potency and a symbol of an erection.

Rhodiola rosea

Rhodiola rosea grows in Siberia and is also known as golden root and has been used by the native population to increase vigour and enhance sexual stamina. Rhodiola rosea treats stress and stress is one of the main causes of malfunction in the bedroom. It has been used as a medicinal plant over the years. It was first recognized by the Greek physician Dioscorides, 77 B.C.E, for its healing properties. The plant has also been part of the traditional medicines of Russia and Scandinavia. Since the early 1700s it was used to help with stamina, to boost sexual desire and to treat impotence. Rhodiola rosea became such a legendary invigorating agent that Chinese emperors sent expeditions to Siberia to gather the root, which can be taken in teas and supplements. In Siberia it is traditional for married couples to receive a bouquet of Rhodiola rosea roots on their wedding night as a gift of love; because the root increases stamina and fertility.

Rice
According to Hindu erotology an effective sexual remedy included rice. A drink made from sparrows eggs and rice, boiled in milk, to which you add honey and ghee. Wild rice mixed with honey of equal weight should be eaten in the evening according to the Hindu *Ars Amatoria* and the *Ananga Ranga.*

Rice Oil
Rice oil is extracted from the fresh leaves of a plant called ruta graveolens; it is said to have an effect like cantharides. (See Cantharides)

Rocket
(Brasica eruca) Ruler Mars, Rocket is a species of cabbage that is grown in the Mediterranean and often used in salads. The plant rocket has been especially celebrated by the ancient poets for possessing the virtue of restoring vigour to the sexual organs. It was consecrated to Priapus and was grown around the sites of his statues. Ovid called rocket salacious and Marital the Roman epigrammatist says that it invigorates amorous desire. Rocket is delicious in salad garnished with oil, seasoning and garlic. It is mentioned by the Roman poet Horace as an aphrodisiac. Columella the Roman poet said of it. "To rouse to duty husbands who are slow."

Roe
Fish roe, in particular cod and herring, are considered aphrodisiac.

Rose
(Rosa Spp) Ruler Venus, in aromatherapy rose oil is used for its calming and relaxing properties. It is also well known as an aphrodisiac, especially in combination with sandalwood oil in massage. A few drops of the oil in your bath water are also beneficial for both male and female sexual problems. The ancient Greeks said that the rose was formed from the body of a dead nymph that the goddess Chloris, goddess of flowers, found in the forest. When Chloris called on the other gods to aid her in creating the flower, Aphrodite gave the rose the

gift of beauty surpassing all others, the three
Graces gave the gifts of youthful blossoming,
brilliance and joy, and Dionysus gave it an
intoxicating nectar and perfume. Finally
Chloris crowned the flower with dew drops and
declared it Queen of the Flowers.
Victorian women used to pick petals from the
most fragrant roses and cover them with egg
whites beaten in water. Then they dusted them
in superfine sugar to crystallize them and dried
the petals on parchment in an oven, these were
then given as love gifts to their suitors.
Magically the rose can be used in many
operations. It is especially suited to love magic and can be used in
philtres, pot pourri and sachets to draw love. It can be used as incense
while you bathe in water infused with rose petals, and sleep with a
sachet of petals beneath your pillow to gain prophetic dreams about
your present or future lovers. It is said that Cleopatra welcomed Marc
Anthony into her chamber with rose petals more than a foot deep
covering her floor; she also soaked the sails of her ship in rose water to
perfume the breezes and announce her arrival.
You can use different coloured roses for different spells; choose red
rose for passionate sexual love, white roses for secrecy, and spatial
love; also to bring peace and harmony to the marital home; pink roses
for tender feelings and perhaps a first love affair; yellow roses for
mental and intellectual attraction and perhaps also for jealousy. (Also
see musk rose)

Rosemary
(Rosmarinus officinalis) Ruler the Sun. Rosemary is an aromatic shrub
indigenous to Southern Europe. The leaves are used medicinally in
perfume and cookery. It was known to the Romans and reputed as an
aphrodisiacal stimulant; it aids circulation throughout the body.
Rosemary can be used in cold drinks as flavouring in water, but the best
aphrodisiac effect results from taking a rosemary bath, this stimulates
the brain, circulatio and, skin and increases sensibilities. (6-8 drops of
essential to a full sized bath)

Rue

(Ruta graveolens) Ruler the Sun. Rue like the water lily, endive and lettuce is believed to have an anti-aphrodisiac effect.

Rye Pollen

(Secale cereale) Extracts from the pollen of certain plants, especially rye can reduce symptoms of prostrate enlargement and will help where the urinary tract has become blocked thus making erections more comfortable.

Safflower

(Carthamus) Safflower is a thistle-like plant that was highly recommended as a sexual stimulant in the 4th century.

Saffron

(Crocus sativus) Ruler the Sun.   Saffron, the dried pistils of a crocus are considered a powerful aphrodisiac in Egypt, Greece, Spain, India and China. It is traditionally taken to maintain sexual performance in males and in cases of general debility. Saffron was used by the ancient Phoenicians as a love spice to flavour the moon shaped cakes eaten in honour of Ashtoreth, the goddess of fertility. According to an ancient legend, a Greek girl partaking of saffron for an entire week could not resist her lover. In high doses the essential oil has obortifacient and toxic properties. Saffron is also a bridal spice and is used as a dye for foods. A potion made from saffron, orange blossoms, dried dates, anise, wild carrots, and egg yolk, boiled in clear water into which honey and the

251

blood of two freshly killed doves have been poured is recommended by Arabs as a potent sexual de-inhibitor.

Sage

(Salvia officialis) Ruler Jupiter, Sage is a well know culinary herb traditionally associated with a long, healthy life. Sage is used to help reduce excessive sweating and is a popular herbal remedy treating menopausal hot flushes and night sweats. Best used as a tea or in capsules. Agrippa said, "That if women cannot conceive, by reason of the moist slipperiness of their wombs, shall take the juice of sage with a little salt which will help them retain the child." The hydrosol is a woman's friend, it can help with period cramps, bloating, PMS and water retention, use as a compress. Clary sage is a euphoric and antidepressant; some find it an aphrodisiac. It promotes feelings of wellbeing. Do not use clary sage essential oil with alcohol. Sage is reputed to have an incredible effect on human females, and is used in love philtres by men and lesbian women to make themselves irresistible to the woman they desire. To make the best use of the herb, dry it and pound it to a powder in your mortar as you chant:

> Sage is love and lust and life
> Bring (name of woman) to be my wife.

Put the powder in a clear glass bottle or jar and place this on your windowsill where it will be in full, direct sunlight for ten days. Keep this safe especially for love potions and philters. One of the best ways to utilise it is to go and visit your lady friend on the day before her menstruation starts. Put a little of the powdered sage beneath your tongue and she may well be unable to resist you.

Saint Damian

See Damian

Saint Johns Wort

See Hypericum

Salep

Salep is a jelly-like preparation made from the dried root of the orchis morio, which is the Turkish Satyrion. It is used in the Middle East as a drug and food. In Turkey, Iran and Syria salep is popular as a sexual restorative.

Salmon

As with most fish, salmon is considered an aphrodisiac.

Salt

In the Middle Ages salt was believed to be an aphrodisiac. It was associated with the goddess Venus, the goddess of love who was said to have arisen from the sea. Hence originated a widespread epigram,

> In Venice why so many whores abound?
> The reason sure is easy to be found,
> Because, as learned sages all agree,
> Fair Venus' birthplace was the salt, salt sea.

Salvia

Salvia is a genus of the sage family, used for garnishing, it also has a reputed aphrodisiac value.

San Pedro Cactus

(Trichocereus pachonoi) This cactus grows in South America and can reach 20 feet (6 meters) tall. It has a beautiful white scented flower that opens at night. The cactus has been used ritually and medicinally since ancient times. Fresh slices of the cactus are used to brew a drink that is used in shamanism to produce visions and healing trances. It is also well known as an aphrodisiac.

Sandalwood

(Chandana Sanalum album) Sandalwood is a wild-growing tree with scented leaves which is often used in aromatherapy. It is an important ingredient in several aphrodisiac recipes.

Sandix Ceropolium

In earlier periods sandix ceropolium was a plant accredited with exciting the senses and stimulating a desire for intercourse. Tiberius the dissolute Roman Emperor is said to have exacted a quantity of the herb from the Germanic tribes as a tribute. According to Dr Venette, it was used in Sweden to stimulate husbands in their matrimonial duties.

Sandalwood

Santonin

(Artemisia maritime) Santonin is a drug once used as an aphrodisiac. It is extracted from the dried flower heads of the plant Artemisia named after Queen Artemisia, wife of King Mansolus, who reigned in the 4th century B.C.E. The plant grew on hills and valleys, in the frontiers of Turkistan. Nomadic tribes used the herb for medicinal purposes.

Sassafras Tree

(Sassafras albidiuim) The slender sassafras tree is also called fennel wood, it grows in Northwest America and has large oval egg shaped leaves. The Indians of North America consider the tree sacred, and use it for 'good medicine'. It is venerated as the 'tree of love'. The root cortex is used to make powerful love drinks and the oil is used in erotic massages. Sassafras is a component of the 'love drug' MDMA.

Sarsaparilla

(Smilax officinalis and many others) Sarsaparilla also popularly known as smilax, belongs to a group of climbing perennial vines that are armed with prickly spines and are found in tropical and subtropical areas of the world. The dried, thick rhizomes and slender roots are widely used in herbal medicine. Sarsaparilla has been used as a male pro-sexual herb since ancient times; it was introduced to Europe in the 14th century by the Spanish. Sarsaparilla is used to increase low sex drive in males and to help overcome impotence and infertility because it aids testosterone production in the body. It can be used in lower doses in women to boost low sex drive and help with menopausal symptoms.

Satibo

Satibo is a very popular supplement that claims to help men and women; it contains the following major ingredients: Chinese yam, Wolfberry, Liquorice, Job stears, Gorgon fruit and Lily. The manufacturers claim that its erection speed is quicker than Viagra and the feeling of erection is stronger. Satibo capsules have been used extensively throughout Asia and the Middle East for many years, and the product is now rapidly gaining popularity in the western world. It was believed to have been invented round 2,000 years ago, for a Chinese Emperor, in his passion to satisfy the ladies in his court - three thousand of them. How did the Emperor have the energy to satisfy so many ladies? He asked his top herbalist to make some pills for him so that he could keep his strength of body.

Satureia
Otherwise known as the plant savory, used by the Romans as an aphrodisiac. (Also see savory)
Satyrion
(Orchis mascula) Satyrion is an aphrodisiac cited by Theophrastus to possess wonderful properties to generate in a man the ability to accomplish the act of love twelve times successively. Speaking of this plant, Venette said "that the herb which the Indian King Androphyl sent to King Antiochus was so efficacious in exciting men to amorous enjoyment as to surpass in that quality all other plants".
Sauerkraut
According to researchers in Pittsburgh, sauerkraut has a definite pro-sexual action for males. They claim that sauerkraut's high content of vitamin C and lactic acid is responsible for increased sexual activity.
Savory
(Satureja Montana) Ruler Mercury, The Romans cultivated this pungent herb, which they called 'satureia' only for its supposed aphrodisiac qualities. It was usually taken with honey, which could be mixed with wine. This herb was also advocated by the poet Ovid as a sexual stimulant. Use savory hydrosol diluted as a wash for sexually transmitted diseases, fungal infections and vaginal or urinary tract infections. Regular use boosts immune function and used with cinnamon and oregano hydrolates, can enhance the libido.
Saw palmetto
(Sabal serrulata; Serenoa repens) The saw palmetto is a small palm tree that is native to North America and the West Indies. It has hands of yellow-green leaves and ivory flowers that set an edible dark berry fruit with a nutty, vanilla flavour. Saw palmetto has long been used as a male tonic, sexual rejuvenator and aphrodisiac. The North American Indians used it in magical love drinks. Saw palmetto is widely used to improve impotence and low sex drive in men, as it has estrogenic actions; it is also used to stimulate breast enlargement in women.
Scammony
Scammony is a gum resin indigenous to the Middle East, it is used in medicine. Compounded with honey, scammony is recommended as an aphrodisiac by Avicenna.

Schisandra

(Schisandra chinensis) Schisandra, also known as 'magnolia vine', is an aromatic woody vine native to North Eastern China. It is a popular Chinese tonic herb also known as wu wei zi or five flavoured fruit as it simultaneously tastes salty, sweet, bitter, sour and pungent. It was commonly used by Taoist women to enhance their sexual energy. Like ginseng, Schisandra has powerful adaptagen properties and appears to be a true pro-sexual herb; it helps the body to adapt and cope with stress and is well known as a sexual tonic that reputedly increases secretion of sexual fluids in men and women. Schisandra berry tea is drunk in China to increase vaginal lubrication and sexual desire and by men to improve sexual stamina.

Scopolia

(Scopolia camiolica) Scopolia is an herbaceous annual that grows in Southeast Europe, it has purple bell-shaped flowers. The root was used as a poison and to prepare magical love drinks, it has also been used as a substitute for mandrake. This is a dangerous plant and if used as an aphrodisiac it could kill; bringing a new meaning to 'a little death'.

Scots Pine

(Pinus Syllvestris) Used as a hydrosol it is one of the best general tonics and an effective immune system stimulant. The essential oil has a mild hormone-like effect on the endocrine system and will improve physical and mental strength. Scots Pine improves stamina generally and should be used in baths and saunas.

Screw Pines

(Pandanus species) There are some 600 species of *Pandanus* that grow in Asia and Africa; the fruits are large and brightly coloured. On the Seychelles the aerial roots of the vacoa, which resembles an erect penis, are considered a potent aphrodisiac.

Sea Bean

(Canavalia maritime) Sea bean is a squat bush found in South America and Africa; they have red flowers and bean like fruits. The beans have been used in Africa for thousands of years as an aphrodisiac and have been found in prehistoric graves. They are also smoked as a marijuana substitute together with the dried leaves. In Peru the plant has been used in rural magic and sex rites.

Sea Holly

In the 17th century an English apothecary named Burton, from Colchester, produced aphrodisiac confections derived from sea holly roots.

Sesame

Sesame seeds were widely used in the Orient to promote fertility, an Arab powder made from sesame, ginger, cloves, nutmeg, coriander, cardamom and lavender was widely used as an aromatic aphrodisiac in ancient times.

Sea slug

The sea slug, *drepang,* a Malay term, is a species of *holothuria* found in the Red Sea and Oceania. On manual contact the sea cucumber shaped object expands, symbolic of genital erection. Among the Arabs it is a highly popular aphrodisiac. They are also greatly prized by the Chinese, to whom it is exported after the drepang is dried in the sun.

Sensitive plant

(Lajjalu Mimosa Pudica) The sensitive plant responds to touch and is found in many places in India, Africa America and Brazil. The Sensitive plant is widely used for urinary complaints and bleeding disorders such as menorrhagia, (Abnormally heavy bleeding at menstruation). The seeds help to increase the production of semen and provide vigour and vitality for men, the sperm count is also increased. It is also used in the treatment of leucorrhoea, (a whitish or yellowish discharge of mucus from the vagina).

Shallot

Shallot is a small onion, used in sauces and salads. It was considered as an aphrodisiac by Martial the Roman epigrammist. "If envious age relax the nuptial know, thy food the scallions and thy feast shallot."

Sheep

Sheep's trotters steeped in vinegar were given to newly married couples as a love aid on their honeymoon.

Shell Fish

As with fish most shell fish are considered as aphrodisiacs. The Greeks in particular are fond of shell fish in love feasts.

Shrimps

Shrimps contain phenylalanine, an amino acid that actively promotes sex drive.

Shvadaustra

Shvadaustra has a reputation in Hindu erotic manuals as a drink for increasing sexual vigour. The drink contains the guduchi plant, asparagus, racemosus, liquorice and long pepper boiled in ghee, milk and honey; usually taken in the spring to wake up the sexual impulses after winter.

Siberian ginseng

(Eleutherococcus senticosus) Siberian ginseng is a deciduous, hardy shrub native to Eastern Russia, China, Korea and Japan, and is related to genuine ginseng (Penax ginseng) and is also known as devil's root or taiga root and sometimes called wucha. Famous Chinese herbalist Li Shi-Chen said in his herbal medicine treatise Ben Cao Gang Mu. "I would rather have a handful of wucha than a cartload of gold and jewels." It was first discussed as a valuable medicine over 2,000 years ago in the herbal thesis *The Divine Husbandman's Classic of the Materia Mediaca*, which refers to the root of Siberian ginseng as a panacea for maintaining health. For this reason it was regarded as a treasure by the ancient sages. Its root has similar actions to the root of Korean and American ginsengs, but it is not closely linked. Siberian ginseng has been used in the Orient for over 2,000 years. It is often regarded as an inexpensive substitute for Korean ginseng but it has a remarkable range of therapeutic uses.

Siberian ginseng is widely believed to increase one's zest for life and is noted for its aphrodisiac properties. It has oestrogen-like activity and has been shown to relieve hot flushes, vaginal dryness, night sweats and anxiety. It is also said to improve fertility by enhancing overall vitality and regulating sex hormones. In men it can give higher sexual energy and prolongs an erection and it is safer than Viagra.

Silk-Cotton Tree

(Bomba Malabaricum) Silk cotton is a big tree that grows in India, Sri Lanka, Indonesia and Malaysia. It has a resinous bark which produces a substance called moca-rasa. It also has red flowers and large seeds. The bark is used to prevent premature ejaculation and to promote the thickness of semen; it is said to further virility.

Skink

(Scincus officinalis) The skink is a small lizard, indigenous to Arabia and North Africa. It has been prized as a medicine and is treated throughout Arabia as a potent aphrodisiac when fried in oil. To the

258

Antilles the skink is called 'mahuiha' and 'brocket terrestre' Dr Venette called it the little crocodile.

Skirret

There are references to skirret a plant that has an esculent tuber, by Nicholas Venette, the French physician; he rated it as a potential aphrodisiac. The Roman Emperor Tiberius imported this plant from Germany for his sexual orgies.

Skullcap

(Scutellaria sp.) The mushroom Skullcap works as a tonic to the mind and nerves; skullcap generally soothes and relieves tension. It is excellent for women's problems such as PMT and menopause; and is colloquially called 'bitchwort'. It is considered a sexual relaxant for women. Take as a tea or tincture.

Snails

The Romans used the necks of snails taken in a little wine as an aphrodisiac. Roman poets mention snails and the French regard them as a food of love. One recipe goes as follows; Snails boiled with onions, parsley, and garlic then fried in olive oil, then boiled again in strong red wine.

Snake

During the Renaissance, philtres in France called goblet d'amour were obtainable from apothecaries, witches and occultists; they often contained the heart and tongue of a viper, or the blood and hair of a red headed woman.

Snuff

According to Sheik Nefzawi in *The Perfumed Garden* snuff acts as an aphrodisiac. Sneezing has been compared to a mini orgasm.

Soma

One Hindu prescription recommended to achieve sexual potency and strengthen the libido consisted of the juice of the fruits of the cassia fistula, enugenia jambolana, mixed with powder of the soma plant, vernonia anthelmistica the eclipta prostata, the lohopa, jihirka; all indigenous plants to India.

Soup

Soup, particularly fish soup, has often been in the menus for love feasts. Fish soup in Hindu erotology is assumed to have aphrodisiac value. Other soups that are popular are onion soup, mushroom soup and celery soup.

Southenwood
Ruler Mercury, Southenwood was mentioned by Pliny the Elder author of *Historia Naturalis* as a sexual aid if the plant is placed under the bed, the southernwood is also used in charms against conception.

Spanish fly
Mignot says that; Ferdinand the Catholic of Castile owed his death to the effect of the philtre administered to him by his Queen Germaine de Foix in the hope of enabling him to beget an heir to the crown of Argon, Navarre and Naples. Spanish fly has long been known to increase sexual desire, arouse the female libido and even improve the female orgasm. Spanish fly, which is actually the emerald-green blister beetle, is found in the southern parts of Europe. The crushed and dried body of the beetle was used as a diuretic and irritant, but was also used as a very potent aphrodisiac. Spanish fly has been used as a powerful aphrodisiac for hundreds of years with great success. It works by irritating the urogenital tract and producing an itchy feeling in the sensitive membranes inducing a feeling that allegedly increases the woman's desire for sex. Some evidence finds that Spanish fly can be dangerous, especially for men, use extreme caution if you decide to try it.

Sparrow
It is reputed that male sparrows were eaten to produce a heightened sexual awareness. This is probably why we don't see many sparrows these days!

Spearmint
(Mentha viridis) Ruler Venus, this mint is the variety used mainly in savoury cookery, most especially mixed with sugar and vinegar to make mint sauce, which is considered to be an aphrodisiac by some.

Sperm
The Romans used deer sperm as an aphrodisiac.

Spinach
Spinach, rich in iron, can help to maintain the male erection.

Squash
(Curcubita pepo) The squash was cultivated by the North American Indians; it has large round fruits and yellow flowers. The seeds are eaten and used medicinally and were long considered an aphrodisiac. Ayurvedic and Tantric system have long valued the seeds; they belong to the class of vajikarana (aphrodisiacs) that are consumed during

Tantric rituals of love.

St. Ignatius' Beans

(Strychnos ignatiii) The beans grown in the Philippine Islands; from this bean strychnine was isolated in the 19th century. They are a dangerous poison, reputed to have aphrodisiac qualities, not proven.

Stinging Nettle (see Nettle)

(Uritca dioica)

Stinkhorn

(Phallus impudicus) This fungus is often found in the forests of Germany and has become well known because of its shape and its smell. It looks like an erect white penis and for this reason the stinkhorn is also known as phalloid fungus. It has been called 'witches' egg' or 'devil's egg' and is an ancient aphrodisiac which was praised as early as Wolfram von Eschenbach's '*Parcival*'.

Storgethron

Storgethron is a plant used in Greece as a love tonic; it has been identified with the common leek.

Stramonium

(Dataura stramonium) This plant, sometimes called 'thorn apple' or 'datoula' in Turkish, is a strong narcotic drug; largely used in the Orient. Stramonium seed, mixed in wine, produced a sexual stimulus but is very dangerous as an over dose will kill.

Strawberry

Ruler Venus. Strawberries are known as the 'fruit of Venus', the Roman goddess of love. They are regarded as an aphrodisiac, especially when combined with champagne. (Try chocolate coated strawberries.) The oil can be used in perfumes and baths to attract love, or to awaken passion, use a little of the oil in an evaporator for spells to awaken sexuality. The oil can be placed in sachets to attract a sexual liaison.

Strombus

Some species of strombus found in the Black Sea were used by Somali women as an aphrodisiac according to Dr Jocobus X.

Sturgeon

Sturgeon soup is considered to be an aphrodisiac in the Mediterranean area.

Sunflower

(Helianthus annuus) The sunflower, ruled by the sun, has been cultivated for over 3,000 years by Indians in Mexico. It has long been

used as a remedy and food and the oil is now used all over the world. The ancient Mayans made an extract of the petals, which they drank as an aphrodisiac.

Surag

Surag is a root that, according to Leo Africanus, is a strong aphrodisiac.

Sweet Flag

(Acorus Calamus) The sweet flag grows over the temperate world in marshes, and the borders of streams and ponds. It has an aromatic odour when bruised and the leaves are sword-like in shape, the flowers are greenish-yellow in colour. Calamus has been used for over 2,000 years by the Chinese, the Moso sorcerers of Yunnan and in Ayurvedic medicine. The roots of the plant were used widely by the American Indians of Canada and the United States as a medicine, the fresh root was chewed, powdered and smoked. The Cree Indians of Alberta would chew a piece of root to overcome fatigue and produce hallucinations and for enhancing sexual stamina.

sweet flag

Swallow Nest Soup

Birds' nest soup is popular in China as a sexual restorative.

Swan

The genitals of a male swan have been used in cooking as an aphrodisiac.

Sweet Basil (see Basil)

(Ocimum basilica)

Sweet Potato

(Ipomoea batatas) The delicious sweet potato forms long turnip like roots and has been cultivated by the Indians of South America for many thousands of years. It is eaten boiled, baked or fried and has a reputation as a female sexual stimulant and as a remedy it is useful for women in menopause or with menstrual problems.

Syrian Rue

(Peganum harmala) Syrian rue, also known as 'harmel weed', is a bushy shrub found in desert or desert like regions, the small fruit contain dark brown seeds. Since ancient times the plant was known as a folk medicine and was used for religious and magical ceremonies.

Shamans inhale the smoke in order to enter an ecstatic state. The aphrodisiac affect of the plant, in particular the seeds, is well documented.

Tabernamontana Coronaria
(Costus arabicus, flacourtia cataphruacta) A Hindu manual suggests a powder composed of tabernamontana coronaria, applied to the wick of a lamp that burns with oil of blue vitriol the resultant black pigment or lamp black, applied to the eyelashes has, apparently, a seductive effect on the observer.

Tarragon
Tarragon is a plant local to Southern Eastern Europe the aromatic leaves are used in salads. It is also reputed to be of aphrodisiac value.

Tea Shrub
(Thea Sinensis) The tea shrub originates in China but is now cultivated throughout Asia and has been used as a tonic drink for more than 3,000 years. Tea was popular among the Taoists as a stimulant and an aid to contemplation and meditation. It was also used as an aphrodisiac, usually in conjunction with other substances, such as ginseng or opium.

Telephilon
Telephilon was mentioned by the Greek poet Theocritus, the leaves of a flower used by the boys of Crotona as a love prophesy. A leaf was placed in the palm of the hand or on the arm and then struck sharply, a crackling sound, as a result, portended a good omen. Telphilon has been identified as a kind of pepper tree or a poppy seed?

Theophrastus
Theophrastus is an Indian herb theme as recounted by Venette which was sent as a gift to King Antiochus; it is reputed to act as a powerful aphrodisiac.

Thorn Apple

(Datura stramonium species) The thorn apple grows worldwide it has prickly fruits and the pale blue flowers have a deliciously inebriating scent and the capsules filled with shiny black seeds. There is also a Mexican variety called the datura ceratocaula that has a smooth fruit. All varieties are traditionally thought to have aphrodisiac value. The name datura originated from early Arabian names such as datura and tatorah. In India women known as mundane ladies (prostitutes) would use 'knockout drops' for intoxicating and robbing their clients. It is also supposed to be an ingredient in the

Cross-section of the thorn apple fruit

making of witch's flying ointments alongside deadly nightshade; this is described by Carlos Castaneda in the *Teachings of don Juan* in which the agent known as 'the little smoke' was used for astral travel. The use of thorn apple can be very dangerous and cause blackouts, heart attacks and hallucinations.

Thyme

(Thymus vulgaris) Ruler Venus, this fragrant herb has long been used for medicinal purposes and in cookery it has also been favoured as an aphrodisiac.

Tomatoes

Tomatoes originate from South America where they were first cultivated by the Aztecs. Legend has it that in the 16th century a Spanish priest brought tomato seeds to Seville from Peru. They had such a positive effect on those who ate them that the French referred to them as pommes d'amour, or apples of love. Once called Peruvian Apples and grown as purely ornamental plants, tomatoes, originally a native of South America, are now cultivated throughout the world. Together with many other exotic imports the tomato gained a reputation as an aphrodisiac. The herb basil was said to be an aphrodisiac, has a unique affinity with tomatoes, which deserve the name 'love apples' when sprinkled with this fresh herb.

Tongkat Ali

(Eurycoma longifolia) Tongkat Ali root is one of the most powerful aphrodisiac plants on earth and is a tree that grows in Malaysia, Burma and Thailand. It is used to treat malaria, high blood pressure and fatigue as well as loss of sexual desire. Southern Asian men enjoy tongkat ali in a plethora of forms; tea, oil and a supplement for its sex enhancing properties. The preparation jamu is a traditional sex stimulant in which Tongkat ali is the primary ingredient. The root is said to contain properties that inhibit aging and it significantly boosts sex drive and function in men and women, by increasing testosterone; which is a key factor in increasing sex drive in men and women.

Tonka

Tonka is a drug that is obtained from the Tonquin beans, the ripe seeds of *Coumarouna odorata*. They have a fragrant aroma but are bitter to the taste. Tonka is used to flavour foods, and is believed to have mild aphrodisiac properties.

Tortoise

The tortoise with its characteristic protrusion of the head and neck was a symbol sacred to Venus, it represented the procreative principle. Gypsy legends hold that baked tortoise and the hedgehog have aphrodisiac properties.

Trapa Bispinosa

Trapa bispinosa is a plant used in Hindu aphrodisiac concoctions. The roots or seeds of the plant were used with jasmin, kasurika and liquorish and an onion like bulb named kshirakapoli, powdered and mixed with sugar, milk and ghee. The mixture is then boiled and the resultant paste is then taken as a beverage. Trapa bispinosa is a nut of the same species as water chestnut, which is indigenous to India and Southern Europe.

Tribulus

(Tribulus terrestris) Tribulus terretris is an Indian plant, also known as ci ji li, Used in Ayurvedic medicine. Its fruit contains furostanol saponins that are used to treat male genital or uruinary problems, low sex drive and impotence. Tribulus helps men with low testosterone levels.

Tripe

Tripe is a food believed to be a sexual stimulant in some circles.

Truffles

Truffles are the next most famous aphrodisiac food after oyster. They have an odour reminiscent of the pheromone given off by male pigs, hence they are readily snuffled out by amorous sows. Both the white and black variety are said to be potent. The truffle is an edible fungus, indigenous to Europe, known to the Romans as a sexual inducement it is often used for stuffing game. Napoleon was advised by one of his generals to eat truffles to increase potency. P.J. Amoreux was a French naturalist and physician of the early 19th century was author of *Opuscule sur Les truffes*, a translation from the Latin of the 16th century. Alphonsus Circarellus relates the value, both gastronomic and amatory value of truffles. A famous French gourmet of the early 19th century, author of *Physiology of Taste*, of truffles he says, "It makes women more amiable and men more amorous". George IV highly appreciated the virtues of truffles, and gave his foreign ministers special directions in the courts of Turin, Naples, and Florence to forward any truffles that might be found superior in size, delicacy and flavour to the Royal kitchen.

Turmeric

(Curcuma longa) Turmeric is a substance derived from the curcuma, the saffron plant, considered an efficacious stimulant but mostly used in curry. In India is highly prized as a love stimulant and it is also used as a vaginal douche!

Turnips

A famous French writer on gastronomy Brillant-Savarin applauded the potency of this recipe as an aphrodisiac; turnips, chicken, ground beef, parsley all cooked separately then mixed together and boiled. Turnips stewed in a milk sauce, has been recommended as helping potency in men.

Turtles Heart

Turtles Heart are an exceptional anti-aphrodisiac if carried in a wolf's skin, it was also used as a charm to stop someone cheating.

Uchchata
The root of the Indian plant Uchchata, piper chaba, and liquorice, mixed with sugar and steeped in milk produce a beverage that is in Hindu erotology, alleged to promote sexual vigour.

Urid
Urid seeds are a kind of chickpea or gram, used in Indian cookery. The Hindu manual *Ananga-Ranga* recommends them for regaining sexual prowess. Urid seeds are steeped in milk and sugar, the mixture is left in the sun for three days, reduced to a powdery form, kneaded into cakes and fried in ghee, the cakes are then eaten each morning for the best results.

Valerian
(Valeriana officinalis) Ruler Mercury, Valerian is a perennial herb that has long been used as an aphrodisiac, Celtic women wore a sprig of valerian between their breasts to attract lovers, while witches used cetwale to entice young men into their beds. Later it became known as 'drunken sailor' and was used by tavern prostitutes. Valerian was used as an aphrodisiac and is available as an herbal infusion but it is mostly recommended as a sedative and an aid to sleep these days.

Vanilla
(Vanilla planifolia)
Vanilla is a climbing plant that grows in Central America and has white flowers. Vanilla is said to be a potent aphrodisiac and is widely used in perfumery and aromatherapy. The effects of its sensual aroma may be intensified by eating vanilla flavoured confections. Vanilla comes from orchids. It was one of Madam Pompadour's favourite aphrodisiacs, together with celery and chocolate; not all at the same time I hope. She also favoured chocolates spiced with vanilla and amber. Vanilla oil is used as a base in perfumery, flavouring and has always been considered a powerful stimulant.

Vatodbhranta
For erotic stimulus one love manual suggests an application of a mixture of the leaf of the plant vatodbhranta, flowers thrown on a human corpse, the powder of peacock bones and the jiwanjiva bird.

Veal
Veal sweetbread is mentioned in some manuals as a sexual aphrodisiac.

Venison
Venison is often referred to as an aphrodisiac.

Vervain
(Verbena officinalis) Ruler Venus. This perennial plant grows in hedges and along walls; it likes waste areas and rough ground. The pale blue flowers and all the other parts of the plant are used in medicine. Druids called the plant 'legend plant', 'ironhard' and 'wonder plant'. It is said the plant would lend the penis the hardness of iron, making it 'ironhard'; often used in some spells and sex magic.

Vuka Vuka
First used by Lobengula the famous African King, and now enjoyed by men everywhere. Vuka-Vuka is available for men and women in convenient tea sachets, tablets, capsules, drops and cream. Recommended for women too who need a dietary supplement to boost their stamina and sexual excitement. This is a blend of natural herbs that has been based on a formula used by generations of African men to nurture and enhance the pleasure and responsiveness of their wives. This combination of natural ingredients has been especially formulated for this purpose. Ingredients: Guarana, Damiana, Centella Asiatica and Schizandra.

Walnut

Ruler Sun, Walnuts are used magically to regain vitality. They are particularly useful to those who have been burning the candle at both ends, or who are exhausted from sexual overindulgence.

Water Cress (Also see cress)

Ruler the Moon, Water cress works on the urinary system and is useful in the regulation of women's courses. An ideal component of salad for a love feast mixed with other herbs and salad plants.

Water Lily

Monks, nuns, and clerics of all degrees used to drink daily for twelve days on end a concoction consisting of water lilies and syrup of poppies. This drink was believed to deprive the person of desire for sexual congress.

Wheat

(Triticum aestivum) Ruler Venus, Wheat is a grain that was first cultivated over 6,000 years ago. The plant dries out after the grains have ripened. The medicinally valuable wheat germ has long been used for skin conditions and in massage. There is some investigation on wheat as a love aid due to the high content of vitamin E.

White Musali

(Asparagus adscendens) The Musali is a long thin and thorny plant which grows tall and erect; its leaves grow in tufts on the stalks. It is native to India and the Himalayas. The plant is helpful to the reproductive system and is a useful aphrodisiac as well as an aid to increasing the sperm count.

Wild black cherry (see cherry)

(Prunus sertina)

Wild Lettuce

(Lactuca virosa) Ruler the Moon. This biennial herb grows in fields and prairies in Europe and North America. The flowers are light yellow and spiky, a milky sap flows throughout the entire plant and is exuded when it is damaged. Wild lettuce is a tranquilizer and helps with sleep problems. The sap was collected by North American Indians who made incisions into the plant. The sap was smoked in the sacred pipe as a ritual and sexual stimulant. The thickened sap is also known as lettuce opium, compass plant or lopium. Wild lettuce is said to  stimulate logos or sexual energy and bring one closer to a higher consciousness and it is used in the yoga discipline of kundalini. Wild lettuce is also a natural sedative and helps restful sleep.

Wild Yam

(Dioscorea villosa) Wild yam is a Mexican perennial vine with heart shaped leaves and small green flowers that is native to North and Central America. It has been used medicinally by American Indians, the Maya and Aztecs to relieve colicky pain, impotence and to boost libido. It is high in sex hormones such as testosterone and oestrogen, and this may account for its ability to boost sex drive in men and women. It is often used as a hormone replacement remedy because of is progesterone like action in the body.

Wine

A Roman saying held that "Venus is lonely without Ceres (bread) and Bacchus (wine)". White wine with juniper berries, Calisaia, which is a species of Peruvian bark, bitter quassia. The liquid is filtered and then mixed with bitter orange syrup. A glass taken daily acts as a strong aphrodisiac. Francois Villon, the medieval Bohemian, favoured hippocras as a drink conducive to laughter by day, and sport and caresses and kisses all night. The Romans took wine in moderation and it was considered an aphrodisiac, Petronius wrote of it in the *Satyricon.*

An ordinary beverage attributed with aphrodisiac benefit was old wine containing the pungent root of the plant pyrethrum or pellitory, as was the gentian wine made from gentian root. The Marquis de Sade advocated large amounts of alcohol of all sorts in his amorous banquets. The Roman epigrammist Martial stated that too much wine could have the opposite effect and this is the case with too much of any alcohol. Hindu literature also condemns excessive wine drinking in connection with sexual congress. A drinking rule runs thus,

> So long as the steadfast look wavers not,
> So long as the mind's light flickers not,
> For so long drink! Shun the rest!
> Who so drinks still more is a beast?

Willow
(Salix alba) Ruler the Moon, the pounded leaves of the willow in a drink is said to be an anti-aphrodisiac.

Witch-Hazel
(Hamamelis) Witch Hazel has, in the past, been considered an erotic inducement if applied externally.

Woodcock
Woodcock has been long been considered an aphrodisiac and is reputed to boost seminal fluids.

Wood Rose
(Argyeia nervosa) Wood rose is a vine found in the dry tropics of Hawaii and South and South East Asia. The plant has heart-shaped leaves and funnel-like flowers. The seeds are said to have aphrodisiac qualities and are the main ingredient in the infamous bliss balls.

Wormwood
(Artemisia absinithium) Ruler Mars. Wormwood grows in most parts of the world and has a leafy flower stem, it has a very bitter taste and a characteristic odour. It was dedicated to the Ancient Greek Goddess Diana, who was also called Artemis hence the name of herb Artemisia. In England the plant is called 'Green Ginger' and 'Old Woman'. Wormwood branches were used in love magic. In Mexico the dried leave were smoked in place of marijuana and were reputed to produce euphoric and aphrodisiac feelings. In the Middle Ages when sorcery and witchcraft were more extensive, spells were frequently cast on a victim's virility. To counteract such a malefic condition, wormwood was used as an antidote. In the 19th century absinthe, a wormwood based liqueur, was the favourite of the bohemians. It was said, after prolonged use, to drive you mad; but had the reputation of an aphrodisiac.

Xoanon

Xoanon was a primitive wooden image of a deity supposed to have fallen from heaven used in sex magic.

Yagé

(Banisteriopsis caapi M) Yagé is a vine that grows on trees in the Northern jungles of South America. It has pink flowers and a reddish brown winged seed. The Indian tribes of the South American Orinoco and Amazon basins use yagé in their ceremonies. The Tukanoans of Colombia administer the drug to adolescent boys to fortify them for the ritual of entry into manhood. The narcotic drink is a hallucinogen and is used for magic, prophecy and divination. In Brazil and Peru, yagé is  used in religious ceremonies and witch doctors use the plant to diagnose and to treat illness and impotence.

Yarrow
(Achillea milleforlium)
Ruler Venus. Yarrow is a scented perennial herb used in love magic, if tickling your true love's nose with a yarrow stem causes a nose bleed then he or she will always be faithful, a painful experiment but one with a reasonable probability of success as yarrow stems can be quite hard and brittle. Yarrow was often used by medieval witches and for wedded couples it was believed to ensure seven years of devotion and faithfulness. North American Indians have used the plant for many years and consider it sacred; it is even consumed as a tea in support of the vision quest. The Navajo Indians esteemed the plant for its aphrodisiac properties. They drink a tea made from the plant or chew the raw stem one or two hours before intercourse. In ancient China the stem was used in geomancy, especially in the I Ching oracle.

Yeast
Yeast used medicinally is believed to possess aphrodisiacal properties.

Yerba Maté
(Ilex paraguariensis) Yerba maté is a slightly smoky tree that only grows in the rainforest of Paraguay, sometimes just referred to as maté, its leaves made into a tea for a nutritional food and stimulant. According to an ancient legend, the sacred formula for preparing the leaf of Yerba maté was revealed from Heaven as a reward for faithfulness and to protect against infirmity.

Ylang Ylang
(Cananga odorata) The ylang-ylang tree grows in Southern Asia and has long yellow flowers with heart-shaped petals. The flowers produce a strongly aromatic oil that is used in massage and the scent is very aphrodisiac to men and to women. Put 6 to 8 drops, not more, in a bath in preparation for lovemaking. The oil can be used to help impotency, frigidity and depression.

Yohimbe and Yohimbine
(Pausinystalia yohimbe, Corynanthe yohimbe) Yohimbe is a pro-sexual herbal supplement made from the bark of a tall, evergreen tree native to the West African counties of Cameroon, Zaire and the Congo. It is used by many Africans and is one of the most potent aphrodisiac herbs, used over the years, especially by the Bantu to increase sexual desire, enhance sexual pleasure, and boost sexual performance and to treat impotence.

273

Zallouh

(Ferulis Harmonis) Zallouh grows in the mountainous areas of the Middle East, and has been revered since ancient times; zallouh is a small shrub with thin leaves and tiny white or yellow flowers. Goats are said to seek out the plant before they rut and the root of the plant has been used as a sex enhancer for thousands of years. Zallouh has a strong tradition of use by men with erectile problems, and by men and women with low libido. One story says that around 1000 BCE king Solomon and Makeda the Queen of Sheba built a temple near the base of Mount Haramoun to honour Zallouh. Also according to legend the women of the harem prepared infused goblets of Shirsh Zallouh for King Solomon's pleasure; this drink is said to have imbued the king with extraordinary virility, enabling him to have sex with several wives per night. Zallouh has been proclaimed an 'herbal Viagra' or a 'sexual fountain of youth' by a report on CNN.

Zinc

Zinc is vitally important to healthy sexual functioning and although other factors must be taken into consideration, zinc deficiency can be the cause of impotence, low sperm count, depression, mood changes and sub fertility. And for women during breast feeling and child bearing; tiredness, lethargy and depression can result. Every time a man ejaculates he loses 2.5 mg of zinc. Zinc is very important to the functioning of the immune system and prolonged deficiency of zinc can lead to real problems for both men and women.

Appendix 1

A Guide to the Use and Preparation of Herbs, Charms and Oils used in Aphrodisiacs

In this chapter I will explain some of the terms such as incense, potion, philtre and perfume, then demonstrate how herbs in general can be used in different ways.

Charm bags, Gris-Gris, Sachets

The Gris-Gris, Sachet or Charm Bag is a form of amulet or talisman which is created to be carried by a person, or placed in a certain place in order to gain a specific magical effect. It can contain a single object or several, such as herbs, oils, resins or a power object, some thing personal from the intended recipient, or even written spells.

The making of a charm bag is a magical operation and as such should be carried out in a sacred area. For example if making a Gris-Gris to incite lust in the recipient, or in a specific person who will come into contact with the wearer, herbs and roots which might be included are almonds, pine, basil, poppy seeds and myrrh resin. Plus a small piece of amber as a power object and some form of representation of the genitals. A woman could use a belemnite to represent a male penis, while a man could use a hag stone, a natural holed stone, to represent the female vagina. (Editor's note - remember - it is wrong to try to remove another person's choice. Magic may well rebounbd on its creator.)

The only difference between a Gris-Gris and a sachet is that a sachet contains no power objects and a sachet is usually sealed and left in a particular place, usually hidden.

Elixirs

These are herbs infused in either alcohol or a mixture of wine and alcohol. Sometime instructions are given in the text for elixirs from certain plants detailing the method of brewing and type of alcohol. These are generally taken a drop of two at a time, or as a drink in wine, spirits or mead. But as with every new substance that you decide to take internally try it cautiously and be very sure that the substances you have chosen to use are not helusagenic, toxic or poisonous.

Hydrosols

Hydrosols are made from the left over water after producing essential oils and can have many of the same properties as concentrated essential oils, they make good toners and sexual washes.

Incense

Incense is a substance that makes fragrant smoke, you can make your own incenses, the easiest way is to use charcoal discs containing saltpetre. These discs must be used on a heat resistant surface or in a proper thurible as they do generate a lot of heat. In order to light the stick it should be over a naked flame such as a match or candle. Use tongs to do this as the discs can become very hot very quickly. The disc will sparkle and smoke and you will be able to see the ignition taking place as a band of sparks which rush across the surface of the disc. When an area is glowing red then the disc is lit.

Many substances which can be used singly or in combination to make incenses for many purposes are mentioned in this book, however ingredients for your aphrodisiacs can be found all around. As an experiment go outside and pick some leaves, flowers or twigs. Try to use ones you can identify so that you are able to recognise them to use again. For example leaves of cinquefoil and silverweed have a sweetish aroma, sage, rosemary and thyme are herby; beech and rowan leaves and twigs have a woody autumn scent; apple and pear twigs smell fruity. The best incenses are resins such as pine or frankincense; they will be a sticky gunge that will harden if you gather it on a twig.

If you want to blend incenses, herbs should be ground up finely; wood made into small shavings, seeds pounded or they may explode, resins left as small lumps. Mix the ingredients together and add some drops of essential oil before placing on your charcoal disc.

Oil or Perfume

There are two forms of oils which are primarily used in aphrodisiac preparations or love enchantments, these are the pure essential oils of the plant or resin and infused oils. Essential oils are basically the pure oily essence which is pressed from the herb and should contain no adulterants. They must always be diluted in neutral carrier oil and you will thereafter be able to create perfumes of whatever strength you require by simply diluting the essential oil for yourself. (Usually 1-5 drops of essential oil to 5 ml of carrier oil).

Infused oils are made from neutral vegetable oils which have had the appropriate herb, flower or resin placed in them to infuse their perfume to the carrier oil. Making your own infused oils can be a good way of obtaining substances which are not generally available or are prohibitively expensive.

To make your own oils, pour 50 ml of good quality vegetable oil into your mortar and add 2 tablespoons of the herb, root, flower (flower petals will need more) or resin and pound this into the oil. Put the resulting mixture into a bottle and store in a dark warm place for three days. On the fourth day strain the mixture and check whether the perfume is strong enough for your purposes. If it is not strong enough repeat the process with a further 2 tablespoons of herb and leave an additional three days.

Ointment or Balms

Ointments are a solid way of using and storing herbs and they are usually made to rub into the skin. One would use a solid base of cream, petroleum gel, Aloe Vera gel, lard or solid vegetable oil. You would melt the base in a double boiler and add very finely chopped and ground herbs to the liquid base and pound the herb into the oil. The mixture will solidify. Then return the mixture to the heat. When it has re-melted, you may add a little simple tincture of benzoin (1 drop to every 5 ml of mixture) or some other essential oil. This acts as a preservative and helps prevent the ointment going off. Finally, sieve the oil through a stocking or fine net into a jar and leave to set. For more solid ointment add a little melted beeswax of paraffin wax at the first stage of melting the base.

Philtres and Powders

A philtre is any powdered herb which is taken internally, in minuscule doses a pinch at a time, a powder is not always taken internally but can instead can be sprinkled on clothes, around the home, or in a place where someone or something will come into contact with it, philtres can also be used in this way.

Pot Pourri

A pot pourri is a modern way to use herbs for ritualistic purposes; it is very simple to do. Take a selection of herbs, spices and oils for the purpose you require and make a fragrant mixture. Leave this mixture in a bowl in your room to create an appropriate atmosphere. Mixes can be purchased now quite easily but experiment and make up your own mixes from dried flowers, pine cones, bits of bark, fruit peel and shells.

Potion, Brew, Tea, Infusion or Decoction.

A standard brew or infusion for the majority of herbs is made from 25 ml dried herb or 75 ml fresh herb in one litre of water. Bring water to the boil and pour it on the herb. (Approximate measure 25 drops = I ml. 1 teaspoon = 5 ml. 1 table spoon – 15 ml.) The brew can be taken hot, or you can cool it and keep it either in the fridge, or frozen into blocks in the freezer. Standard dosage is 1/2 a cup a day.

A tisane or herb tea is a weaker infusion made by using 1 teaspoon full of the dried herb in a mug of boiling water.

A brew or potion will usually refer to a tisane or infusion. A decoction is usually made from the root of a plant or from wood and consists of adding 1 ounce root or wood to 1 pint boiling water. This is then simmered until the liquid has reduced by half. This method is therefore

278

used only on substances which are tough, if used on normal herbs the prolonged boiling will often destroy many of the properties you wish to make use of, therefore use a tisane or infusion unless otherwise stated.

Smoking

There are two types of smoking involved in sexual ritual practise, one method is smoking a herb in a pipe or rolled into a cigarette, and inhaling the smoke as one would use tobacco. The other way to use smoke is to wash or cleanse the body, a room, house or magical equipment. To magically cleanse something or to imbue it with the powers of the particular herb, the process is often called 'smudging'.

Smudging

Smudging is a way of using the smoke from burning herbs as a way to cleanse the body, an object, or a given area of negative influences. I myself use smudging to "cleanse" my therapy room and crystals before using them in healing, and for protecting my home. The theory behind smudging is that the smoke attaches itself to negative energy and as it clears it takes the negative energy with it, releasing it into another space to be regenerated. The skilful use of sage could help in warding and banishing ceremonies as well, if used properly and with reverence. You can, and should, regularly smudge your meditation area, your altar if you have one, and any object that you use for healing, both before and after use. This ensures that the healing object will be able to do its job with the least amount of interference from dead energy that may be holding it back.

Steam

Steaming is a good way of using the perfume of herbs, but this time without burning them. Traditionally herbs are placed in water in a cauldron, which is either suspended above a fire, or stood at one edge amongst the embers. As the water comes to a boil it gives off a perfumed steam which can be inhaled, or used to cleanse the body, for divination or creating a romantic or calming atmosphere. You can burn herbal steamers which are powered by a candle beneath a bowl. Oil evaporators are more often used today, water with a few drops of essential oil in it being put in the upper bowl over a nightlight candle.

Essential oils can also be put in your bath or left in bowls or warm water in the room to scent the air and provide a romantic or sensual atmosphere.

Wash Waters

Wash waters are a diluted infusion of herbs that are used to bath in or wash down large areas. Wash waters are in general used for psychic cleansing, consecration and to banish unwanted vibrations, but they can also be used to attract certain influences or set moods.

Appendix 2

Parts of the Body in Relation to Star Signs

Aries	Head
Taurus	Neck
Gemini	Hands, shoulders, arms
Cancer	Solar plexus Stomach
Leo	Heart, Back
Virgo	Lower stomach
Libra	Lower back
Scorpio	Genitals, belly
Sagittarius	Thighs
Capricorn	Ankles, heels
Aquarius	Calves
Pisces	Feet

Appendix 3

Glossary of Words

Adrenergic: Pertains to that transmission of information throughout the nervous system that is moderated by the adrenal hormone adrenaline.

Algolagnia: A term that includes the two sexual perversions of masochism and sadism.

Anal aphrodisiac: Stimulating the erogenous zones on the anus; certain substances have specific effect on the sphincter muscle.

Anaphrodisiac: Having a suppressing effect upon the desire for sex.

Androstrerone: A male sexual hormone.

Anomaly: Deviating from the norm, malformation.

Anthelmintic: An agent that expels or kills parasitic worms.

Anticholinergic: Preventing or blocking the formation of the neuro-transmitters acetylcholine and choline; many substances traditionally used as aphrodisiacs have this effect.

Antisphilitic: An agent used to combat syphilis.

Arteriosclerosis: A condition characterized by a thickening or hardening of the arteries.

Asarone: Asarum camphor, a plant substance that is transformed into a psychedelic and aphrodisiac phenthylamine. (TMA) by an endogenous process of animation.

Astringent: Having the property of constricting the tissues of the mouth.

Ayurveda: The ancient Indian science of life healing and medicine.

Biogenic: Produced as a result of life processes.

Buttons: Dried slices cut from a peyote cactus.

Cunnilingus: Oral stimulation of the female genitalia.

Decoction: The boiling of herbs and drugs in order to produce a concentrate.

Dildo: A synthetic penis, used for self-gratification.

Diuretic: An agent that causes urination or stimulates kidney activity.

Dysmenorrhoea: Painful or difficult menstruation.

Emmenagogue: To induce a period or menstruation.

Endemic: Native, limited to an area.

Enema: A liquid preparation intended for injection into the rectum or lower intestine tract.

Enzyme: A biocatalyst; effect metabolic processes in the organism.

Ephedrine: A plant substance used as the model for amphetamine.

Estrogen: A female sexual hormone.

Fellatio: The oral stimulation of the penis.

Flagellation: The act of sexual stimulation by means of whipping.

Frigidity: Lacking friendliness or sexual enthusiasm.

Fumigation: The ritual use of smoke to purify or perfume a person or place.

Galactogogue: Inducement to flow of milk.

Geriatrica: A medicinal agent used to rate the effect of age; many aphrodisiacs appear to have generally beneficial effect upon ailments due to age.

Geomancy: Soothsaying, divining, or interpreting objects.

Gonorrhoea: A sexually transmitted disease.

Herpes: Genital herpes is a powerful virus and once it has taken hold it can remain in the body for years to come, tending to flare up when you are under stress or suffering from depression. As genital herpes and cold sores of the mouth are caused by the same virus it is very dangerous to indulge in oral sex if either partner has a cold sore.

Hedonistic: Relating to pleasure; hedonism is the philosophy of pleasure.

Hepatitis: Inflammation of the liver.

Homeopathy: A system of medical practice that is based upon the focused administration of extremely minute concentration of drugs and plant materials.

Hydrosol: A flower water, such as rose water, frequently a by product of the manufacture of essential oils.

Ibogaine: A plant substance that has anti-depressive, monoamine oxidase inhibiting, psychedelic and aphrodisiac effects.

Indication: A sign that suggests the proper treatment for a disease.

Irritation: Inflammation, soreness, or physical discomfort in a part of the body.

Ithyphallic: An artistic representation of an erect phallus.

Libations: Sacrificial rites in temples, usually involving liquid like wine.

Luteinizing hormone: A gonadotropic HVL hormone that stimulates the intestinal cells.

Maceration: An extract of a drug made at room temperature by steeping in water or some solvent like alcohol.

Menorrhagia: Abnormally heavy bleeding at menstruation.

Mycelium: The subterranean root mass of a fungus.

Neuralgia: The acute pain in an area innervated by a sensory nerve.

Neurotransmitter: a chemical information carrier in the nervous system; endogenous neurotransmitters are secreted within the body; many psychedelic and aphrodisiac substances are exogenous neurotransmitters.

Orchitis: Inflammation of the testis.

Pruritus: Itching that can pertain to the anus or the genitals. It can be caused by external irritation, insufficient hygiene after using the toilet, by wearing jeans or underwear that is too tight, for example or by the inappropriate use of perfumes or deodorants on these delicate areas.

Priapic: Pertaining to the ithyphallic god of fertility, Priapus.

Priapism: An abnormal, pathological stiffening of the penis; can result in damage to the corpora cavernosa.

Prolactin: a hormone that induces lactation; produced in the interior lobe of the pituitary.

Psilocin: A psychedelic substance of the tryptamine group found in certain fungi.

Satyr: Ithyphallic; lusty god who is one of the followers of Dionysus and Bacchus.

Testosterone: A male sexual hormone.

Tincture: A preparation produced from fresh or dried plants by means of extraction.

Tonic: An agent that invigorates or strengthens; many aphrodisiacs are considered to be tonics.

Transvestite: A man who likes to dress up in female attire.

Urtication: A treatment employing stinging nettles; an old remedy for invigorating the sex life and combating impotence.

Appendix 4

Dictionary of Bizarre Sexual Practices

Agalmatophilia: Attractions to statues or mannequins.

Anasteemaphilia: Attraction to a person because of a difference in height.

Axillism: The use of the armpit for sex.

Chrematistophilia: Arousal from being charged for sex or robbed.

Dacryphilia: Arousal from seeing tears in the eyes of a partner.

Dendrophilia: Attraction to trees.

Emetophilia: Arousal from vomit or vomiting.

Formicophilia: Enjoyment of the use of insects for sexual purposes. (Or the arousal from having sex on a cheap counter top)

Macophilia: Arousal from the sight of a high-end Macintosh.

Nasophilia: Arousal from the sight, touch, licking, or sucking of a partner's nose.

Oculolinctus: The act of licking a partner's eyeball.

Sacofricosis: The practice of cutting a hole in the bottom of a front pant pocket in order to masturbate in public with less risk of detection.

Siderodromophilia: Arousal from riding in trains.

Taphephilia: Arousal from being buried alive.

Appendix 5

Horny Goat Weed

While travelling in South Africa we passed through a village that was selling large carved cockerels. Well, in South Africa every roadside has people selling carvings, hats and almost everything, but I had not seen any other place where they were selling cockerels. So I asked the guide why they were selling cockerels in this particular village.

"That's because of Rasputin." He said.

"Who was Rasputin?" I asked.

"Well there was this farmer and his old cockerel was getting very old and could not service the hens any more. So the farmer went to the local market to buy a new cockerel. When he got to market he found the trader and said

"I need a new cockerel because mine is too old."

The trader then said, "I only have three cockerels at the moment come and look and take your pick."

So the farmer goes into the enclosure and sees three cockerels. The first cockerel is a big blue black chap who looks very proud and is strutting around the pen his name is King. The second cockerel is a glossy red colour and looks very haughty and powerful. His name is Nero.

The third cockerel is a brown, skinny, tatty moth eaten looking creature pecking away at the weeds in the corner of the pen. His name is Rasputin.

Farmer Jones looks at the three cockerels and decides to take King as he looks a proud strong chap.

So the farmer pays the trader and takes King home and puts him in with the chickens.

King's pecker comes up and he dashes around the hen house giving all the hens a good seeing to. Then he promptly drops dead. That's no good thinks the farmer he goes once round the hens and drops dead he must have had a weak heart. So the following morning he takes the dead King back to the trader and explains what has happened.

"Well." says the trader "I am sorry you had better take one of the other cockerels in exchange."

So the farmer goes again into the pen and looks at the two remaining cockerels. He looks at Nero and thinks he looks strong and powerful.

"I will take Nero." He tells the trader. So he takes Nero back to the farm and puts him in with the hens.

Nero's pecker comes up and he dashes into the hen house but he runs straight past all the hens and runs up to the old cockerel and starts giving him a good old seeing to. Nero shows no interest in the hens. 'Well that's no good', thinks the farmer he must be a gay cockerel. So the next morning the farmer takes Nero back to the trader and explains what has happened.

"Well I'll be." says the trader "You had better bring him back and I will exchange him. But I only have Rasputin left."

The farmer goes into the pen and looks at Rasputin still nibbling away at the weeds in the corner of the pen. He still looks skinny and tatty but the farmer thinks, well he is the only one left and he can only be any better that the last two, so he decides to take him.

So he takes Rasputin back to the farm and puts him in with the hens. Rasputin's pecker comes up and he dashes into the hen house and he gives every one of those hens the best time they have had in a very long time. There are clucks and grunts and after about an hour there are a lot of hens lying around with their feet in the air looking exhausted.

But Rasputin barely looks winded. Rasputin's nose comes up and looks around and sees that over the fence are the farmer's free-range pigs. Over the fence he jumps and starts to have sex with the pigs. Well there is squeaking and squealing and to cut a long story short those pigs have never had such a good time, even when the farmer would bring the old boar round once or twice a year. At the end of an hour the pigs are all lying on the ground with contented sighs. But Rasputin hardly looks exerted; he puts his head up and sniffs the air and starts looking around again.

Just down the lane is Farmer Smuts' prize dairy herd and off goes Rasputin in that direction. Farmer Jones follows, but by the time he reaches Farmer Smuts' farm Rasputin has found the cows in the barn and there is mooing and lowing and all sorts of havoc going on, Daisy, Clover and Dandelion have never had such a good time. Farmer Jones arrives and Farmer Smuts is furious

"Some bloody cockerel has just come in and ravished all my prize cows."

"Where did he go?" says Farmer Jones.

"He went off over that way towards old Farmer Burton's ostrich farm." Says Farmer Smuts.

"Oh no." says farmer Jones as he rushes off down the road.

He hears the commotion long before he reaches Farmer Burton's ostrich farm. There was all sorts of hullabaloo going on and he can hear an outraged farmer Burton shouting and yelling. By the time Farmer Jones reached the ostrich farm there is no sign of Rasputin.

"Where did he go?" farmer Jones splutters.

"That darn cockerel, he ran off towards the water hole." Replies Farmer Burton between gasps of fury.

Off goes Farmer Jones towards the water hole and then he sees Rasputin lying on the ground near the water hole. He must be dead from exhaustion thinks the farmer, well he was a game old bird I can't just leave him there to be eaten by hyenas; I'll take him home and give him a decent burial.

So Farmer Jones starts off towards Rasputin. As he gets nearer he hears Rasputin say out of the corner of his beak:

"Go away, the vultures will be down in a minute".

The next day Farmer Jones goes to see the trader to tell him what had happened.

"What did your feed him on?" said Farmer Jones.

"We never fed him", replied the trader, "He just ate the weeds in the corner of the pen."

"What do you call those weeds?" Farmer Jones asked.

"Horny Goat Weed." Replied the trader.

Bibliography

Anand, Margo, *The Art of Sexual Ecstasy*, Thorsons, 1990.

Bagwan Dash Dr, *Indian Aphrodisiacs*, Lustre Press, Roli Books, 2001.

Brewer, Sarah Dr, *Increase Your Sex Drive*, Thorsons, 1999

Brook Jasmine *Spells for Love and Success*, Abbeydale Press, 2001.

Catty Suzanne *Hydrosols, the Next Aromatherapy*, Healing Arts Press, 2001.

Davenport John, *Aphrodisiacs and Love Stimulants*, Luxor Press, 1965.

Eason Casandra, *A Magical Guide to Love and Sex*, Piatkus, 2000.

Harvey Karen, *The Kiss in History*, Manchester University Press. 2005.

Kilham, Chris, *Hot Plants*, St Martins Griffin, 2004

Lacroix Nitya, *Sensual Massage*, Dorling Kindersley, 1989.

Morris Desmond, *The Naked Woman*, Jonathan cape, 2004.

Papa Jim, *Pape Jim Magical Herb Book*. 1996.

Ratsch Christian, *Plants of Love*. Ten Speed Press, 1997.

Runcie, James, *The Discovery of Chocolate*, Harper Collins, 2001

Seller Wanda, *The Directory of Essential Oils*. Daniels, 1992.

Sempers Chris, *The Magical Herbal Spellbook*, Corvaus Books. 1998.

Simons G.L., *The Illustrated Book of Sexual Records*, Virgin Books. 1982.

Tisserand Maggie, *Essence of Love*, Harper SanFrancisco, 1993

Wedeck. H. E., *Dictionary of Aphrodisiacs*. Bracken Books. 1962.

FREE DETAILED CATALOGUE

Capall Bann is owned and run by people actively involved in many of the areas in which we publish. A detailed illustrated catalogue is available on request, SAE or International Postal Coupon appreciated. **Titles can be ordered direct from Capall Bann, post free in the UK** (cheque or PO with order) or from good bookshops and specialist outlets.

A Soul is Born by Eleyna Williamson
Angels and Goddesses - Celtic Christianity & Paganism, M. Howard
The Art of Conversation With the Genius Loci, Barry Patterson
Arthur - The Legend Unveiled, C Johnson & E Lung
Auguries and Omens - The Magical Lore of Birds, Yvonne Aburrow
Asyniur - Women's Mysteries in the Northern Tradition, S McGrath
Beginnings - Geomancy, Builder's Rites & Electional Astrology, Nigel Pennick
Between Earth and Sky, Julia Day
The Book of Seidr, Runic John
Caer Sidhe - Celtic Astrology and Astronomy, Michael Bayley
Call of the Horned Piper, Nigel Jackson
Carnival of the Animals, Gregor Lamb
Cat's Company, Ann Walker
Celebrating Nature, Gordon MacLellan
Celtic Faery Shamanism, Catrin James
Celtic Lore & Druidic Ritual, Rhiannon Ryall
Celtic Sacrifice - Pre Christian Ritual & Religion, Marion Pearce
Celtic Saints and the Glastonbury Zodiac, Mary Caine
Circle and the Square, Jack Gale
Company of Heaven, Jan McDonald
Compleat Vampyre - The Vampyre Shaman, Nigel Jackson
Cottage Witchcraft, Jan McDonald
Creating Form From the Mist - Wisdom of Women in Celtic Myth, L. Sinclair-Wood
Crystal Clear - A Guide to Quartz Crystal, Jennifer Dent
Crystal Doorways, Simon & Sue Lilly
Crossing the Borderlines - Guising, Masking & Ritual Animal Disguise, Nigel Pennick
Dragons of the West, Nigel Pennick
Dreamweaver by Elen Sentier
Earth Dance - A Year of Pagan Rituals, Jan Brodie
Earth Harmony - Places of Power, Holiness & Healing, Nigel Pennick
Earth Magic, Margaret McArthur
Egyptian Animals - Guardians & Gateways of the Gods, Akkadia Ford
Eildon Tree (The) Romany Language & Lore, Michael Hoadley

Enchanted Forest - The Magical Lore of Trees, Yvonne Aburrow
Eternally Yours Faithfully, Roy Radford & Evelyn Gregory
Everything You Always Wanted To Know About Your Body, But So Far
    Nobody's Been Able To Tell You, Chris Thomas & D Baker
Experiencing the Green Man, Rob Hardy & Teresa Moorey
Face of the Deep - Healing Body & Soul, Penny Allen
Fairies and Nature Spirits, Teresa Moorey
Fairies in the Irish Tradition, Molly Gowen
Familiars - Animal Powers of Britain, Anna Franklin
Flower Wisdom, Katherine Kear
Fool's First Steps, (The) Chris Thomas
Forest Paths - Tree Divination, Brian Harrison, Ill. S. Rouse
From Past to Future Life, Dr Roger Webber
From Stagecraft To Witchcraft, Patricia Crowther
Gardening For Wildlife Ron Wilson
God Year, The, Nigel Pennick & Helen Field
Goddess on the Cross, Dr George Young
Goddess Year, The, Nigel Pennick & Helen Field
Goddesses, Guardians & Groves, Jack Gale
Handbook For Pagan Healers, Liz Joan
Handbook of Fairies, Ronan Coghlan
Healing Book, The, Chris Thomas and Diane Baker
Healing Homes, Jennifer Dent
Healing Journeys, Paul Williamson
Healing Stones, Sue Philips
Heathen Paths - Viking and Anglo Saxon Beliefs by Pete Jennings
Herb Craft - Shamanic & Ritual Use of Herbs, Lavender & Franklin
In Search of Herne the Hunter, Eric Fitch
In Search of the Green Man, Peter Hill
Inner Mysteries of the Goths, Nigel Pennick
Inner Space Workbook - Develop Through Tarot, Cat Summers & Julian Vayne
In Search of Pagan Gods, Teresa Moorey
Journey Home, The, Chris Thomas
Language of the Psycards, Berenice
Legend of Robin Hood, The, Richard Rutherford-Moore
Lid Off the Cauldron, Patricia Crowther
Light From the Shadows - Modern Traditional Witchcraft, Gwyn
Lore of the Sacred Horse, Marion Davies
Lost Lands & Sunken Cities (2nd ed.), Nigel Pennick
Lyblác, Anglo Saxon Witchcraft by Wulfeage
The Magic and Mystery of Trees, Teresa Moorey
Magic For the Next 1,000 Years, Jack Gale
Magic of Herbs - A Complete Home Herbal, Rhiannon Ryall
Magical Guardians - Exploring the Spirit and Nature of Trees, Philip Heselton
Magical History of the Horse, Janet Farrar & Virginia Russell
Magical Lore of Animals, Yvonne Aburrow

Magical Lore of Cats, Marion Davies
Magical Lore of Herbs, Marion Davies
Magick Without Peers, Ariadne Rainbird & David Rankine
Masks of Misrule - Horned God & His Cult in Europe, Nigel Jackson
Medicine For The Coming Age, Lisa Sand MD
Medium Rare - Reminiscences of a Clairvoyant, Muriel Renard
Menopausal Woman on the Run, Jaki da Costa
Mind Massage - 60 Creative Visualisations, Marlene Maundrill
Mirrors of Magic - Evoking the Spirit of the Dewponds, P Heselton
The Moon and You, Teresa Moorey
Moon Mysteries, Jan Brodie
Mysteries of the Runes, Michael Howard
Mystic Life of Animals, Ann Walker
Pagan Feasts - Seasonal Food for the 8 Festivals, Franklin & Phillips
Paganism For Teens, Jess Wynne
Patchwork of Magic - Living in a Pagan World, Julia Day
Pathworking - A Practical Book of Guided Meditations, Pete Jennings
Personal Power, Anna Franklin
Pillars of Tubal Cain, Nigel Jackson
Places of Pilgrimage and Healing, Adrian Cooper
Planet Earth - The Universe's Experiment, Chris Thomas
Practical Divining, Richard Foord
Practical Meditation, Steve Hounsome
Psychic Self Defence - Real Solutions, Jan Brodie
Real Fairies, David Tame
Reality - How It Works & Why It Mostly Doesn't, Rik Dent
Romany Tapestry, Michael Houghton
Runic Astrology, Nigel Pennick
Sacred Animals, Gordon MacLellan
Sacred Celtic Animals, Marion Davies, Ill. Simon Rouse
Sacred Dorset - On the Path of the Dragon, Peter Knight
Sacred Grove - The Mysteries of the Forest, Yvonne Aburrow
Sacred Geometry, Nigel Pennick
Sacred Nature, Ancient Wisdom & Modern Meanings, A Cooper
Sacred Ring - Pagan Origins of British Folk Festivals, M. Howard
Season of Sorcery - On Becoming a Wisewoman, Poppy Palin
Seasonal Magic - Diary of a Village Witch, Paddy Slade
Secret Places of the Goddess, Philip Heselton
Secret Signs & Sigils, Nigel Pennick
The Secrets of East Anglian Magic, Nigel Pennick
A Seeker's Guide To Past Lives, Paul Williamson
A Seer's Guide To Crystal Divination, Gale Halloran
Soul Resurgence, Poppy Palin
Spirits of the Earth series, Jaq D Hawkins
Stony Gaze, Investigating Celtic Heads John Billingsley
Subterranean Kingdom, The, revised 2nd ed, Nigel Pennick

293

Talking to the Earth, Gordon MacLellan
Talking With Nature, Julie Hood
Taming the Wolf - Full Moon Meditations, Steve Hounsome
Teachings of the Wisewomen, Rhiannon Ryall
The Other Kingdoms Speak, Helena Hawley
Transformation of Housework, Ben Bushill
Tree: Essence of Healing, Simon & Sue Lilly
Tree: Essence, Spirit & Teacher, Simon & Sue Lilly
Tree Seer, Simon & Sue Lilly
Torch and the Spear, Patrick Regan
Understanding Chaos Magic, Jaq D Hawkins
Understanding Second Sight, Dilys Gater
Understanding Spirit Guides, Dilys Gater
Understanding Star Children, Dilys Gater
The Urban Shaman, Dilys Gater
Water Witches, Tony Steele
Way of the Magus, Michael Howard
Weaving a Web of Magic, Rhiannon Ryall
West Country Wicca, Rhiannon Ryall
What's Your Poison? vol 1, Tina Tarrant
Wheel of the Year, Teresa Moorey & Jane Brideson
Wildwitch - The Craft of the Natural Psychic, Poppy Palin
Wildwood King , Philip Kane
A Wisewoman's Book of Tea Leaf Reading, Pat Barki
The Witching Path, Moira Stirland
The Witch's Kitchen, Val Thomas
Treading the Mill - Practical CraftWorking in Modern Traditional Witchcraft by Nigel Pearson
Witches of Oz, Matthew & Julia Philips
Witchcraft Myth Magic Mystery and... Not Forgetting Fairies, Ralph Harvey
Wondrous Land - The Faery Faith of Ireland by Dr Kay Mullin
Working With Crystals, Shirley o'Donoghue
Working With Natural Energy, Shirley o'Donoghue
Working With the Merlin, Geoff Hughes
Your Talking Pet, Ann Walker
The Zodiac Experience, Patricia Crowther

FREE detailed catalogue

Contact: Capall Bann Publishing, Auton Farm, Milverton, Somerset, TA4 1NE